'CABLESHIPS'

by

Norman L. Middlemiss

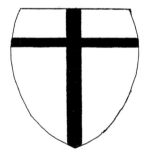

SHIELD PUBLICATIONS LTD

NEWCASTLE - UPON - TYNE

GREAT BRITAIN

ISBN   1 871128 18 8

© First Edition   August,2000 : N. L. Middlemiss

British Library Cataloguing-in-Publication Data

A Catalogue Record is available from the British Library

Published by SHIELD PUBLICATIONS LTD.
P.O. Box 5, Low Fell, GATESHEAD,TYNE & WEAR. NE9 7YS.
Printed by Smith Settle, Ilkley Road, OTLEY.
WEST YORKSHIRE. LS21 3JP.

CONTENTS

Frontispiece : MONARCH (3) completed for H.M. Postmaster General in 1916.
(Swan, Hunter & Wigham Richardson Ltd)

INTRODUCTION

This book on cableships is written and published to commemorate the 150th anniversary of the laying of the first successful submarine cable during 1850/51 from Dover to Calais, with the towed hulk *Blazer* finally achieving success in September,1851. The first attempt to lay a marine telegraph cable had been made on 28th August,1850 by the steam tug *Goliath* between St. Margaret's Bay near Dover and Sangatte on the opposite coast. The unarmoured cable was laid at 4 miles/hour, and slow, clear messages were sent which unfortunately could not be read by the receiver due to retardation of the signal. The successful lay took place on 25th September,1851 with *Blazer* being towed by two tugs with H.M.S. *Fearless* leading the way.

The drawing (right) shows the cable passing through two sets of pulleys onto a small drum before being laid over the stern. The 'brake' for retarding the paying-out is shown operated by the figure in the centre using a simple hand-cranked wooden lever compressor. The expedition took all day due to gales to almost reach the shore at Sangatte, but was short of cable and the connection to dry land was completed during the following month of October by the steam tug *Red Rover*. However when connected to each land terminal at Dover and Calais the cable declined to work due to some unknown reason. Finally on 13th November,1851 the final links were made to obtain clear messages in both directions to end a truly epic and memorable expedition.

The first commercial messages were those sent with share opening and closing prices on the London and Paris bourses, and other messages from both Government and commercial sources ensured the success of the first marine telegraph cable. It should be noted that land telegraphs had been used since 1838 and were first used in 1851 by Northern coal owners to send orders to their agents on the Coal Exchange in London as regards steam colliers.

St. Margaret's Bay near Dover, the British landfall of the early
Cross - Channel telegraph and telephone cables. (Author)

Once the English Channel had been spanned by cable, many cable enthusiasts were
next dreaming of and promoting the idea of spanning the Atlantic with cable in the early
1850s. One of these was **Cyrus Field**, an American who had made a fortune as a paper
manufacturer, another was **William Thomson,** born in Belfast in 1824, who died in late 1901
as **Lord Kelvin.** He was the son of a Mathematics professor, and he studied electric currents
at Glasgow University for the receiving and recording of telegraph messages, and by his
theories pathed the way for the man who actually laid the first Atlantic cable - **Sir Charles
Tilston Bright**. The latter achieved fame at the age of 26 years in 1858 with the completion
of the first but shortlived Atlantic submarine cable, and he is known as the 'father' of submarine
cables. He was born in 1832 and should have attended Oxford University save for his father
losing most of his money, and he had to take paid employment connected with telegraphy.
Cyrus Field came over from America and engaged Bright as Chief Adviser of this Atlantic
project. The Atlantic cable of 1857 was made in two sections with just over half the length
from Newall's factory in Birkenhead and loaded aboard the American frigate *Niagara,* and
1250 nauts of cable made by Glass, Elliott & Company at Greenwich, and loaded aboard the
obsolete sail and steam British frigate *Agamemnon.*

On 5th August,1857 the Irish end of the cable was brought ashore at Valentia and the
next day the expedition set off. The American frigate *Niagara* was to lay the first half from
Valentia, and the British warship *Agamemnon* was to take over in mid-Atlantic and continue
on to Trinity Bay, Newfoundland. After a bad start, they got 380 miles out to sea when the
cable snapped, and the ships had to return to Plymouth leaving the cable on the sea bed. It

was necessary to raise further money to buy 900 extra nauts of costly cable. The ships set off again in June,1858, but encountered a severe storm which lasted all of a week and a lot of Bright's equipment was wrecked with many men injured, and this voyage was also a failure. Another attempt was made at the end of July,1858 with a new cable and the same two ships, both sailing from mid-Atlantic with one landing the cable at Valentia in the east and the other at White Strand Bay near Trinity Bay in Newfoundland in the west. Cables were connected to the shore stations and when tested they worked, and messages of best wishes were sent by the participants to each other on 5th August,1858. The first public message was sent by Queen Victoria to the President of United States of America, and some 732 messages were sent during the two months for which the cable was functioning before it went dead.

Transatlantic submarine telegraphy was thus possible, but the risks were high if a return on investors' money was to be seen in the new underwater cable companies. The British Government also had a financial interest in a cable laid shortly afterwards from Suez to Aden and on to India. This was also a failure, never carrying any messages whatsoever, and before spending any more public money on such projects it was decided that a Committee of Inquiry should be appointed to investigate the whole question of the construction, laying and maintenance of submarine cables. The Committee was authorised during 1859 and its members included five appointed by the Government including **Sir Charles Wheatstone**, the inventor of the first land telegraph, and **Robert Stephenson**, the railway pioneer - who died on 21st October,1859 before the report was published, and four other members appointed by the Atlantic Telegraph Company, which had laid the 1858 cable.

The committee sat from December,1859 to September,1860, taking evidence from many people with experience of submarine cables and making their own investigations, and reported in April,1861. Wheatstone's contribution was a paper of 14,000 words length on the discharge of submarine cables, having tested many samples of differing diameter of core, both copper and iron, and thickness of insulation, in tanks of water. He charged the test cables and monitored the discharge when they were earthed through a galvanometer, and studied the effect of length, core diameter, insulation thickness, conductor resistivity, pressure and temperature on the discharge. At the end of the very detailed report, he referred to several pieces of equipment for measuring the charge on telegraph cables, including his own accumulating discharger, and the way forward to the successful completion of long-distance submarine telegraph transmission.

1865/66 Atlantic cablelaying with the *Great Eastern*

In 1862, the Atlantic Telegraph Company used the powers it had obtained from a new Act of Parliament to issue a prospectus to raise £600,000 in 8% preference shares. By May,1863 they had only raised £300,000 but their consultants Sir Charles Wheatstone, Sir William Thomson and Douglas Galton were sufficiently confident of raising all of the money that they put out tenders for the manufacture of the cable. Richard Glass of cable manufacturer Glass, Elliott had gathered an experienced cable staff in Sir Samuel Canning and Henry Clifford, and won the contract, having come to the conclusion that a concerted attempt by all parties experienced in cablelaying was the only way to sucessfully span the Atlantic. An offer was made to the Gutta Percha company, and on 7th April,1864 the two companies merged under the title of **The Telegraph Construction and Maintenance Co. Ltd** (known as **Telcon** for short). **John Pender**, born in 1815 in Dumbarton, and a very successful cotton merchant in Glasgow and Manchester, became Chairman of Telcon with a capital of £1M with Richard Glass as Managing Director. The Telcon contract to manufacture the cable could now go ahead, but only with a ship large enough to hold the 2,500 nautical miles of cable, and there was only one such ship afloat at the time.

The *Great Eastern* had been designed as a very large passenger steamer for the Australian trade by Isambard Kingdom Brunel, so large that it was forty years after her completion that she was surpassed in her size of 18,915 gross tons on dimensions of length 680 feet, beam 83 feet (118 feet beam over her paddle boxes) and depth of 58 feet with a draught of 30 feet. She was launched sideways at Blackwall on the Thames on 31st January, 1858 and the leviathan was completed in September, 1859 a few days after Brunel had died from the strain of building this huge pioneering ship. She had five funnels, six masts, and 22 compartments within her double iron hull, and two engines, one for the paddles and one for the screw at her stern. She was one of the first big ships built with longitudinal strength as well as many transverse frames and bulkheads to give a series of watertight compartments. Her service speed was 11 knots with a crew of 400, but instead of the expected passenger capacities of 800 first-class, 2000 second-class and 1200 third-class on the Australian trade, she carried very few passengers on the eleven Transatlantic voyages she made as a passenger ship. On 4th April, 1864 she was chartered from lay-up to lay the new Transatlantic cable, and she began a very successful ten-year period as a cablelayer before she was idle again at the end of 1874, being used again for two years from 1886 as an exhibition ship before being broken up at Birkenhead in late 1888.

Her great moment of glory did not come on her first Transatlantic attempt however. The steamer *Caroline* laid the Irish shore end and *Great Eastern* commenced paying out the cable on 23rd July, 1865 on a glorious day, but disaster happened with a broken cable on 2nd August and was lost in 2,000 fathoms of water. The cable was not recovered and the cable team returned home in low spirits, but learnt from their experience and rectified any mistakes in the coiling and laying of the next cable. However this new expense proved too much for the Atlantic Telegraph Company, and in March, 1866 the **Anglo-American Telegraph Company** with a fresh injection of capital took over the Atlantic company. Sir Charles Bright was Chief Adviser of the project, and this fourth attempt to lay a lasting Transatlantic submarine telegraph cable began three months later.

On 30th June, 1866 the *Great Eastern* under Capt. Anderson left Sheerness (the cable had been brought down by barge from Greenwich) and moved down the Thames estuary to the sounds of music. Accompanied by *Medway, Albany* and the warship *Terrible*, paying-out started from Ireland on Friday 13th July - an ill-omened date - but after a struggle the connection was made with the shore end, and later in the day she headed west. Despite two tangles while paying-out which almost snapped the cable, two weeks later on Friday 27th July the *Great Eastern* sailed successfully into Heart's Content Bay, a few miles west of St. John's, Newfoundland, and cheers could be heard from the hills on both sides as well as from ships at anchor in the Bay. When the cable was connected up to the cable house, cable engineers were able to begin transmission of the first messages of this permanent Transatlantic submarine telegraph connection. Special services were then held in several local churches to give thanks for the successful conclusion of this great enterprise that would so much improve the lives of mankind.

GREAT EASTERN at anchor in Heart's Content Bay in 1866.

A typical Atlantic telegraph cable of that time had 700 tons of copper, 350 tons of gutta percha to insulate it, with seven-stranded copper wires known as the core protected by mild steel wire wound spirally around it known as the armouring, and outside of this was two windings of jute, tarred and covered with soapstone. Sir Charles Bright, after his great success with the *Great Eastern*, did much more cable work before he died in 1888, by which time cables had linked most of the countries of the world along the sea bed, passing news and Government confidential information in a world that had at last reduced the huge distances by more or less instant communication. The first small vessel to be permanently adapted for cablelaying was the wooden paddle steamer *Monarch* of 500 tons built in 1830 and modified in 1853. However the majority of cablelaying for the next twenty years was done by temporarily converted vessels. The first ships to be designed as cablelayers were the Tyne-built *Hooper* of 1873 and *Faraday* of 1874; and the Danish-built *H.C. Oersted* of 1872 was the world's first specially designed cable repair ship. *Faraday* was untypical as she had engines aft with funnels abreast, thus leaving the rest of the ship clear for the cable drums and tanks, and a hull in which the stern was almost identical to her bow. *All America* of 1921 (below) shows a more typical cableship design.

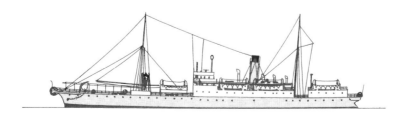

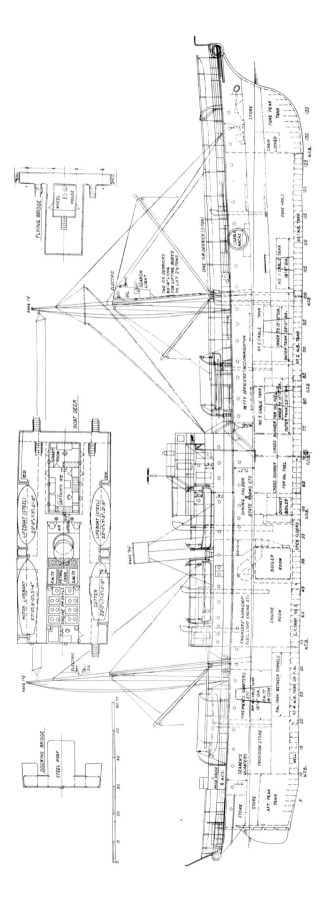

ALL AMERICA OF 1921

The four cable tanks shown in the general arrangement drawing of *All America* of 1921 were designed with three forward and one aft. She had two separate paying-out/picking-up machines forward, from where cable was led by roller fairleads to the stern for stern laying. Cable tanks are fitted in the centre with a truncated cone reaching to within a few feet of the top of the tank, the purpose being to prevent the centre coils bending and collapsing into the centre. Cable coiling begins at the edge of a tank moving towards the cone, and then taken to the outside again. In addition, a horizontal framework known as a 'crinoline' was kept a few feet above the top layers of cable to stop any possibility of a few turns of cable 'whipping' and blocking the entrance to the tank. The cable runs out of the top of the tank along fore and aft troughs when being laid, with the necessary tension on the cable produced by the paying-out machinery and measured by dynamometers, which are in essence electrical strain gauge or load cell devices, and control the laying speed.

Until the recent advent of multi-purpose cableships, most cableships were comparatively small - on average around 1500 grt for inshore work and 8000 grt for deep-sea work. An example of the latter was the Tyne-built *Colonia* of 1902 and 7976 grt, which made the longest lay ever, the Pacific telegraph cable between Bamfield on Vancouver Island and Fanning Island, 1000 miles south of Hawaii, and on to New Zealand and Australia. She was of a similar size as her replacement *Dominia* of 1926 and 9237 grt, which laid a second Pacific cable in 1926. In appearance they resembled yachts with semi-clipper stems and with bow and stern sheaves over which the cable was paid from the large storage tanks in which the new cable was coiled. Cableships in the past were usually painted white or light grey with a buff funnel, and their masts were frequently tall for better reception of radio signals. Private cable and telegraph companies built up their own fleets and Governments also entered the field, the Postmaster General owning ships since 1870.

Bow sheaves were generally used for cablework maintenance operations and stern sheaves for installation. In the past, a standard technique for working over the bow sheaves was to head into the wind and thus keep the ship steady for recovery of cable. Nowadays, this has been replaced by stern-working with computer-controlled dynamic positioning systems to hold the ship exactly in one position. A variety of cable handling machinery has been used over the years for cablelaying with ingenious ways of passing flexible and rigid repeaters, wider than the telephone cable in which they are inserted, over the sheaves. This cable machinery development has resulted in the modern linear cable engines fitted to new cablelayers today. They are also equipped with gear for grappling for and raising damaged cables, and then repairing and successfully relaying them.

When a fault in a submarine cable has been detected, the approximate location of the trouble is found by engineers ashore, who measure the electrical resistance or capacity of the cable up to the fault. The cableship then steams to the estimated position and drops a marker buoy. A grapnel is then dragged at very slow speed across the seabed at right angles to the path of the cable until it snags the cable. The difficult job of raising the cable now begins, as in deep water the strain put on the cable in lifting it would be almost sure to break it, and it is then cut under water and both ends are hoisted on board in turn. Then signals are sent down the cables to the respective shore stations, and the cable from which no answer is received is the section in which the fault lies. Moving slowly towards the fault, the ship heaves the cable on board until the faulty part comes over the bow sheaves and it is replaced with a new part spliced in. After final tests with the shore stations, the two ends of the cable are joined and then dropped to the seabed. Where cables are buried into the seabed for protection against trawling by using **ploughs**, both tracked and untracked **submersibles or remotely operated vehicles (ROVs)** have been increasingly used in modern times to locate and help with the repair of faults.

The crew accomodation of the ships is of a high standard as the work can be irksome and hard. They can steam as low as half of one knot if necessary when paying out cable or grappling to repair a fault, and they hoist three shapes vertically on their foremasts, black between two white. Cableships could be sunk on sight in war-time as they were regarded as ships of war. Some forty ships were chartered during the first thirty years after 1850 for relatively short duration cablelaying expeditions, then once the industry had matured, cable manufacturers and owners began to build up their own fleets of cableships. A list of these chartered ships is given in the Appendix at the end of the book, with the main part of this book concerned with **permanent** cableships, owned by cable manufacturers and cable owners, governments, offshore oil companies, power cable companies, and telecommunications companies. Great Britain led the way in this great cablelaying industry, and the book starts with sections on British cablelayers, with fleet lists in chronological order, and then moves on to the fleets of over thirty other countries of the world that have owned cableships at one time or another.

Submarine telegraph cables became obsolete during the early 1970s, replaced by coaxial telephone cables capable of transmitting thousands of simultaneous telephone conversations, telex (telegram printed on a teleprinter), fax and data streams. The invention of fibre optics created a new submarine cable technology, now capable of transmitting a million simultaneous telephone conversations along one cable. This great upsurge of cablelaying activity since the first operational fibre optic cable was laid in the Autumn of 1986 has seen hundreds of such cables laid in point-to-point, ring, and festoon configurations. This remarkable and happy situation has seen the technological advantage return to 'wire' at the expense of 'wireless' (in the form of satellite communication), although both will be complementary in the future as they have been in the past. By 2003, it is estimated there will be in excess of one million km of submarine optic fibre cable on the seabed, equivalent to more than all of the telegraph and coaxial telephone cable of the past 150 years.

All current and newbuilding cablelayer capacity is chartered for many years ahead to lay the extensive Internet cable spans under the sea, particular for city-to-city links between Europe, North America and the Far East. The graph of worldwide network demand shows a constant level of around 300 terabits/sec for voice traffic, but upwards of 2,500 terabits/sec for data traffic associated with the Internet by year 2002. This can only increase in size beyond that time scale, with many further cableship conversions from ro-ro ships as well as large sophisticated newbuildings. The cableship has thus seen a complete reversal of its fortunes in the last twenty years since 1980 with a current worldwide fleet of one hundred cablelayers and cable repair ships, with many more planned for cable systems still on the drawing board.

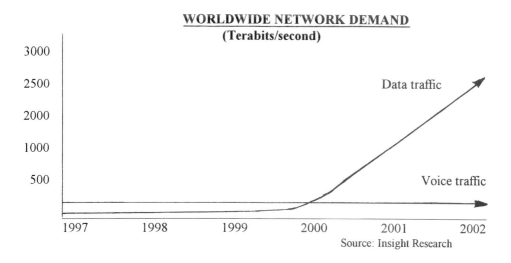

A two-letter code is used for the cableships of each country e.g. GB for Great Britain, US for United States, FR for France, with the cableship fleets of each country following in decreasing numbers order. I have compiled this work from a myriad of sources and wish to particularly mention the excellent book by Kenneth W. Haigh. He died in October,1977 shortly before the second edition of his book was published. He was Officer-in-Charge of the Admiralty Experimental Diving Unit towards the end of his naval career working at Portland Naval Base. His widow continued to live in Weymouth for some time after his death, but despite an exhaustive search no trace of any descendants has since been found. I would also like to thank the many individuals and organisations who have provided information and photographs for this book, in particular Michelle Tenens, formerly Editor of **'Soundings'**, the submarine cable industry magazine, and Barbara Jones and Anne Cowne of **Lloyd's Register of Shipping**, from which the ship data was compiled. Thanks also to Anna Robinson for patiently proof-reading the text, and I wish to particularly thank my good friend Duncan Haws for his 150 excellent scale diagrams, drawn to a scale of 1: 1200, their accuracy greatly complementing the photographs in the book.

Norman L. Middlemiss

Newcastle-upon-Tyne

July,2000

ABBREVIATIONS

CT	Cable Tank
BS	Bow Sheave
SS	Stern Sheave
GRT	Gross Registered Tonnage
DWT	Deadweight Tonnage
G.P.O.	General Post Office
P.T.T.	Post, Telegraph & Telephone
Length x	) Given in feet for ships built
Breadth x	) before 1971, and in metres
Depth	) for ships built after that date

BIBLIOGRAPHY

'Cableships and Submarine Cables' by Kenneth R. Haigh, first edition published in 1968, second edition published in 1978 by Standard Telephones & Cables (S.T.C.)

'Siemens Brothers 1858 - 1958' by J. D. Scott published by Weidenfeld & Nicolson of London in 1958.

'The Thin Red Lines' by Charles Graves published by the Standard Art Book Co. Ltd, London in 1946.

'The Ocean Telegraph to India' by J.C. Parkinson published in 1870.

'Cablelaying in the Pacific with *Anglia* and *Colonia* during 1902/03' by the Chief Cablelaying Officer of the *Anglia*.

'Wireless at Sea - The First Fifty Years' by H. E. Hancock published by the Marconi International Marine Communications Company in 1950.

'British Oceanographic Vessels 1800 - 1950' by Tony Rice published by The Ray Society in London in 1986.

'A Saga of the Seas' by P. B. MacDonald on Cyrus Field and the laying of the first Transatlantic cable, published in 1937.

'Lloyd's Registers of Shipping' Vols. 1850 - 2000.

'Remotely Operated Vehicles (ROVs) of the World' published by Oilfield Publications Ltd.

Various issues of **'Soundings'**, the submarine cable industry magazine originally published by H.M. Post Office later BT (Marine) Ltd, and taken over by Cable & Wireless (Marine) Ltd.

CABLESHIP CHRONOLOGY

1850 28th August: First Dover/Calais attempt by *Goliath* - connection made but message jumbled, unarmoured cable soon hooked up by trawler.

1851 25th September: Second Dover/Calais attempt by *Blazer* - initially unsuccessful but finally connected through on 13th November, 1851.

1853 *Monarch*(1) of 1830 modified to be world's first permanent cableship.
St. Margarets Bay to Belgium cable laid by converted collier *William Hutt*.

1854 Firth of Forth and Firth of Tay cables laid by *Monarch*(1).

1855 Irish Sea cables laid by *Monarch*(1).

1856 Mediterranean and Black Sea cables laid by *Elba* for R. S. Newall & Company.

1857 5th August: Irish end of First Transatlantic cable attempt brought ashore at Valentia using British warship *Agamemnon* - cable snapped 380 miles out, expedition abandoned.
U.S. warship *Niagara* had loaded the other half of the cable.

1858 July: Second Transatlantic cable attempt with *Agamemnon* and *Niagara* - successful. First messages sent from Queen Victoria to U.S. President on 5th August. In total some 732 telegraph messages were sent before the line went completely dead two months later.

1859 December: Public Inquiry into failures of submarine cables after another disaster on a Suez/Aden cable, this time involving public money.

1860 September: Inquiry closed after taking evidence from all with experience of cables.

1861 April: Inquiry committee's findings published.

1862 Atlantic Telegraph Company issued prospectus to raise £600,000 in 8% preference shares for a third attempt at a Transatlantic cable.

1863 May: Some £300,000 had been raised and tenders were sent out for manufacture of third Transatlantic cable.

1864 7th April: Telegraph Construction & Maintenance Co. Ltd (Telcon) formed by merger of Gutta Percha Company and Glass, Elliott & Company. John Pender appointed as first Managing Director.

1865 23rd July: Paying-out commenced on third Transatlantic cable using the *Great Eastern*. *Caroline* had been used for the Irish shore-end. Cable snapped half way across Atlantic, expedition abandoned on 2nd August.

1866 March: Anglo-American Telegraph Company formed to raise fresh finance for a fourth attempt at a Transatlantic cable. 30th June: *Great Eastern* left Greenwich and began paying

out off the Irish coast on 13th July. Finally reached Heart's Content Bay a few miles to the West of St. John's(NFL) on 27th July - the Atlantic had at last been spanned by a lasting telegraph connection !
Hawk purchased by Telcon and converted into a cableship.

1867   *Chiltern* purchased by Telcon and converted into a cableship.

1868   *Investigator* purchased by Telcon and converted into a cableship.
La Plata purchased by W.T. Henley and converted into a cableship.
Malta/Alexandria cable laid for a company associated with John Pender.

1869   *Hibernia*, a former liner, purchased by Telcon and converted into a cableship.
Great Northern Telegraph Company founded in Denmark with telegraph lines laid across Russia and submarine telegraph cable to Japan.

1870   Telegraph Bill of 1868 implemented wherebye all domestic inland telegraph companies nationalised. This included two telegraph companies with submarine cables to the Continent, and the transfer of the converted cableship *Monarch*(1) to H.M. Postmaster General.
First successful France/Algeria cable laid by a British company.
Edinburgh completes conversion to a cablelayer for Telcon.

EDINBURGH was a typical cableship conversion of the mid-Victorian period.

1871   Singapore/Hong Kong cable laid for Eastern Extension Telegraph Company.
French Government succeeds with another British-made cable in spanning the Mediterranean from Marseilles/Algiers, and deploys two maintenance cableships, *Ampere* at Brest for English Channel cables, and *Charente* at Toulon for Mediterranean cables.
Cuba connected to Jamaica, Puerto Rico, Leeward and Windward Islands by the West India & Panama Telegaph Company.

1872 Eastern Telegraph Company formed by John Pender to rationalise his Mediterranean and Middle East cable companies.
H.C. Oersted became the world's first purpose-built cable repair ship for the Great Northern Telegraph Company of Denmark.
Singapore/Banjoewangie/Darwin cable laid by British Australian Telegraph Company and with a landline to Adelaide brings Australia into communication with the rest of the world.

1873 Eastern Extension, Australasian & China Telegraph Company formed by John Pender to cover Far Eastern and Australasian cables.
The Tyne-built *Hooper* became the world's first purpose-built cablelayer for Hooper's Telegraph Works Ltd, Brazilian coastal cables laid on maiden voyage.
International connection to Brazil made by *Seine* from Madeira/St. Vincent/ Pernambuco.

1874 The Tyne-built *Faraday*(1) with double-ended hull became the world's second purpose-built cablelayer for Siemens Brothers. Transatlantic cable laid on maiden voyage.
Norseman(1) purchased by Western & Brazilian Telegraph Company and fitted out as a cableship for maintenance of South American cables.

1875 *Chiltern* present at the bombardment of Alexandria and acted as a terminal station after the cables had been cut ashore.

1876 Australia/New Zealand telegraph connection made by Eastern Extension Telegraph Company. *Kangaroo* and *Seine*, the latter formerly of Royal Mail Line, purchased by Telcon as permanent cablelayers.

1877 *John Pender*(1) converted into a cableship for Eastern Telegraph Company.
Calabria, formerly of Cunard Line, purchased by Telcon and converted into a cablelayer.

1878 New cable repair ships *Sherard Osborn* and *Retriever*(1) completed on the Clyde.

1879 Aden/Zanzibar/Mozambique/Delagoa Bay/Durban telegraph connection made by Eastern & South African Telegraph Company, which had been formed that year.
Scotia, formerly of Cunard Line, purchased by Telcon and converted for cablelaying.

1880 'P-Q' cables laid by a French company from Brest/Porthcurno/Nova Scotia, and Tyne-built repair ship *Pouyer-Quertier* takes up station at Brest.
Grappler completed on the Clyde for West India & Panama Telegraph Company and based in the Windward Islands.

1881 *Hooper* sold to the India Rubber,Gutta Percha & Telegraph Works Company and renamed *Silvertown*. New boilers fitted and sent to West coast South American waters, of great use in sending news back to Europe of the War in the Pacific with Chile the victor.

1882 *Volta* completed for Eastern Telegraph Company, *Viking*(1) for Western & Brazilian Telegraph Company, transferred in 1896 to duties on the Amazon.

1883 *Monarch*(2) completed on the Clyde for H.M. Postmaster General.

1884 Commercial Cable Company formed in New York by John W. Mackay and Gordon Bennett, with repair ship *Mackay-Bennett* completed on the Clyde.
Sisters *Electra, Magneta* and *Recorder*(1) completed for Eastern Telegraph Group.
Magneta lost on maiden voyage Gravesend/Gibraltar.

1885 *Britannia* completed for Telcon as their first specially-designed cablelayer.
American Telephone & Telegraph Company (A.T & T.) formed to raise £300,000 to build a national telephone network, over 3M subscribers in the U.S.A. twenty years later.

1886 Bathurst/Sierra Leone/Accra/Lagos/Bonny telegraph connection made by African Direct Telegraph Company.

1887 *Westmeath* chartered by W.T. Henley to lay cables in the West Indies for a French cable company. Three years later she brings Bermuda into communication for the first time with a Halifax/Bermuda cable.

1888 *Amber* completed for the Eastern Telegraph Company.

1889 Cape Town/Nolloth/Mossamedes telegraph connection made by Eastern & South African Telegraph Company.

1890 *Relay* completed at Sunderland for the Central & South American Telegraph Company.

1891 London/Paris telephone service inaugurated with the Prince of Wales speaking to President Carnot.

1892 *Scotia* lays a cable from Santos to Montevideo, which is already connected to Buenos Aires to give telegraph connection down the whole of the South American coast from the Caribbean.

1893 *Duplex* purchased by Eastern & South African Telegraph Company and converted to a repair ship, based on West coast of South Africa. *Norseman*(2) completed for Western & Brazilian Telegraph Company.

1894 *Telegraf* completed for the Norwegian Government as their first repair ship.

1895 *Francois Arago* linked Madagascar to Mozambique with a French-manufactured cable.

1896 *Contre Amiral Caubet* converted to a cableship for Cie Francaise des Cables Tele-graphiques.

1897 *Grandholm* chartered to lay Manzanillo/Santiago cable for Hooper's Telegraph Works.

1898 *Anglia* completed at Barrow for Telcon as their principal cablelayer.

1899 First American military telegraph cables in the Philippines, followed by cables from Alaska to the Yukon in 1900.

1900 Western Telegraph Company formed by John Pender on East Coast of South America.

The Pacific Cable Board had an 'All-Red' route via the Pacific to Australasia, to complement the 'All Red' route of the Eastern Telegraph Group via the Indian Ocean - both only crossed through British-controlled territory for the land sections.

Boer War cables laid from Porthcurno/Cape Verde Isles/Cape Town by Eastern Group.
John Pender(2) completed on the Clyde as a repair ship for the Eastern Group.

1901 May: First British ship fitted with a Marconi Wireless Telegraph.
December: Marconi sends first Transatlantic radio message to Newfoundland.
Commercial Pacific Cable Company formed.
Mauritius connected to Rodriguez and on to Cocos Island and Perth/Adelaide by *Anglia* as
first cable to connect South Africa to Australia.

1902 *Colonia* completed on the Tyne as Telcon's biggest cablelayer, and she and *Anglia* lay
the Pacific Cable Board 'All Red' cable across the Pacific from Canada to Australia and New
Zealand. *Iris*(1) completed on the Clyde as their repair ship.
8th May: *Grappler* lost with all hands in a tidal wave after volcanic eruption of Mount Pelee at
St. Pierre, Martinique.

1903 *Colonia* and *Anglia* continue Pacific cablelaying with *Silvertown*, this time for the
Commercial Pacific Cable Company from San Francisco/Hawaii/Midway/Guam and on to
Manila and Japan. Sisters *Patrol* and *Restorer* completed on the Tyne for the Eastern Group,
with *Restorer* sold in 1904 to the Commercial Pacific Cable Company as their repair ship.

1904 *Magnet* converted into a repair ship from a coaster at Sunderland.

1905 Brest/Dakar cable for French Government. *Cambria* completed on the Tyne for Telcon.
Wireless Telegraphy Act became law and Marconi's company given licences for all ship-to-
shore communication for eight years.

1906 Sisters *Sentinel*(1) and *Cormorant*(2) completed on the Clyde for the Eastern Group.

1907 *Guardian* completed on the Tyne for the Central & South American Telegraph
Company.

1908 *Patrol* connects Cocos Island to Batavia (Java).

1909 *Telconia* completed on the Tyne for Telcon, and *Retriever*(3) at Goole for the West
Coast of South America Telegraph Company.

TELCONIA of 1909

1910 *Robert C. Clowry* completed at New York as Western Union's first cableship, used for shallow water cable repair.

1911 The last British-owned Transatlantic cable company Anglo-American Telegraph Co. Ltd /Direct U.S.A. is sold to an American combine of Western Union and A. T & T.

1912 First 'continuously loaded' telephone cable in the world on Dover/Calais route for H.M. Postmaster General.

1913 *Edouard Jeramec* completed at Grayville for Cie Francaise des Cables Telegraphiques.

1914 *Transmitter* completed at Goole for Eastern Telegraph Company.

1915 Master of *Levant II* is decorated for bravery while laying a cable from Imbros to Sulva within hours of the first troop landings of the Dardanelles campaign.

1916 *Monarch*(3) and *Lord Kelvin* are completed on the Tyne for H.M. Postmaster General and the Anglo-American Telegraph Co. Ltd respectively.

1917 'Kil' class gunboat *Kilmun* converted for first naval harbour defence cablelaying duties of the Royal Navy.

1918 *Alert*(2) completed on the Tyne for H.M. Postmaster General.

1919 Wireless Telegraphy (Merchant Shipping) Act makes fitting of ship's radio compulsory on all ships over 1600 grt.
Stephan transferred to Britain from Germany as war reparations.

1920 *Lady Denison-Pender* completed on the Clyde for Eastern Telegraph Group.

1921 *George Ward* converted on the Clyde for Commercial Cable Company.
All America completed on the Tyne for All America Cables, which had been formed in February,1920 from existing companies operating from Galveston to Mexico and the West coast of South America.

1922 *John W. Mackay* and *Marie Louise Mackay* completed on the Tyne for Commercial Cable Company. *Norderney* converted from German Navy tanker for Norddeutsche Seekabelwerke.

1923 *Faraday*(2) completed at Palmer's yard on the Tyne as Siemens Brothers cablelayer.
Sisters *Mirror*(2) and *Norseman*(4) completed by John Brown yard at Clydebank for Eastern Telegraph Group.
Dickenson completed at Chester (Pa) for Commercial Pacific Cable Company.

1924 *Cyrus Field* completed at St. Nazaire for Western Union Telegraph Company.
The Cable completed at Alexander Stephen yard on the Clyde for Eastern Extension.
Cable Enterprise(1) completed by Inglis yard on the Clyde for Western Telegraph Co.

CABLE ENTERPRISE(1) at Enderby's Wharf on the Thames.

1925 *Nanyo Maru* completed for the Japanese Government.

1926 *Dominia* completed on the Tyne for Telcon and lays 'loaded' telegraph cable across the Pacific for the Pacific Cable Board.

1927 *Landego* completed as a repair ship for the Norwegian Government.

1928 *Faraday*(2) lays a cable from Beirut to Nabeul in Tunisia for the French Government. *Colonia* sold for conversion to a whale factory ship.

1929 Merger of Marconi's Wireless Telegraphy Company with the Eastern Telegraph Group to form Cable & Wireless Ltd. Severe disruption of telegraphic communication in Western North Atlantic by volcanic movement of seabed between Azores and Newfoundland. Nine cableships from Britain, France and United States sent to repair the cables.

1930 *Ampere*(2) completed at La Ciotat for the French Government. *Matai* completed at the Hawthorn, Leslie yard on the Tyne for the New Zealand Government.

1931 *Faraday*(2) laid up for most of 1930/31. Cable & Wireless Ltd profits tumble to only £75,000 from over £1M at the start of the Depression.

1932 *Faraday*(2) lays a 'loaded' telephone cable from St. Margaret's Bay to La Panne.

1933 *Dominia*, the Telcon cablelayer, laid-up from 1931/34.

1934 Merger talks between Telcon and Siemens Brothers due to almost complete blank order books for submarine cable, with only short lengths of the new 'loaded' telephone cables being required. This led to the formation of Submarine Cables Ltd in the following year and the sale of *Dominia* as there was only enough work for one British cablelayer. *Faraday*(2) was retained as the only British cablelayer.

1935 Bass Strait coaxial telephone cable laid by *Faraday*(2) for the Australian Government.

1936 *Cambria* cablelaying in the Mediterranean.

1937 June: Anglo-Dutch cables laid for H. M. Postmaster General and the Dutch Government. *Toyo Maru* completed for the Japanese Government.

1938 *Lasso* completed for Royal Navy harbour defence cablelaying.

1939/45 The war service of some Allied cableships is now given in some detail :-

Lady Denison-Pender was moved from her base at Aden after Italian bombers attacked the station unsuccessfully on 11th June,1940, and she saw service in the Atlantic, being required at the beginning of 1941 to cut the French-owned Dakar to Brest and Dakar to Noronha cables. She had a lucky escape in convoy from Gibraltar to Freetown, after having successfully completed the laying of a Gibraltar/Madeira cable. She was acting as Convoy Commodore in a small convoy of three merchant ships, all of which were sunk by U-boats including the cargo-liner *Silverbeech*, fully loaded with ammunition. Her enormous explosion left no visible sign of the Silver Line cargo-liner except a huge pall of black smoke with debris raining down on the deck of the cableship and most of her door locks blown off their hinges. One torpedo also passed under the stern of the cableship but she survived, and with no merchant ships left except the rescue tug, she picked up speed and reached Freetown safely. She undertook cable repairs off the West coast of Africa and near Cape Verde Islands, and then proceeded to the East coast of South America for more cable repairs. She then moved into the Pacific via the Panama Canal to operate for several months, returning via Panama to Halifax(NS) where several more repairs were carried out. She finished the war in the West Indies at St. Lucia with a U.S. Navy submarine chaser as protection and on the Brazilian coast without any escort, save for the occasional appearance of an aircraft

Cambria was working with the naval cablelayer *Lasso* at Dover on the outbreak of war in laying anti-submarine indicator loops in the Straits of Dover to the French coast. She was then based at Plymouth for six months from October,1939 in repair work in the Western Channel and the Bay of Biscay. She then repaired Transatlantic cables based at Halifax(NS) before being based in the West Indies at St. Lucia, and later picked up 250 nautical miles of Italian cable off Cape Verde Islands while the enemy was transmitting signals until they were abruptly cut off. This cable was taken into Pernambuco for further use by the Allies, and she then changed crews with *Norseman* at St. Lucia holding a joint ships' concert while in port at Castries. She returned to the Brazilian coast, then worked off West Africa and finished the war at Recife in Brazil. Unfortunately, while at anchor in Montevideo harbour on 8th November,1945 she was run down and sunk by a Uruguayan steamer.

Retriever of 1909 had been moved from her Western Telegraph station in Brazil before the outbreak of war, and sailed to the Mediterranean via the Red Sea, with *All America* chartered to replace her on the Brazilian station. She was chartered for the laying of harbour defence anti-submarine loops in the Mediterranean. While on a voyage from Lemnos to Piraeus, she was bombed and sunk in the Piraeus anchorage on 11th April,1941 with the loss of Capt. Foy and ten of her 46 crew, with another six crew becoming prisoners of war. She had arrived in the anchorage in convoy with one Greek ship and two Greek destroyers, and she cruised between the harbour entrance and the island of Pytalia until attacked by a lone aircraft at midnight. The aircraft raked her with machine gun fire and dropped four bombs, three exploding close alongside the bridge and the fourth blew the bottom out of the forehold and she quickly sank, the survivors escaping in three lifeboats, one of which was holed, and were picked up by Greek destroyers within three hours.

Recorder in the Far East had been moved from Auckland to the Singapore station before the outbreak of war, and with her Chinese crew saw service in the Indian Ocean, Pacific Ocean, at Gibraltar and ended up at Aden at the end of the war. She sailed from Bombay in late 1940 to the Mediterranean and laid some cable off Tobruk in March,1941. She then did a good piece of diversion work, taking 560 nautical miles of Bombay/Aden cable into Muscat in case Egypt was overrun by the enemy and an alternative telegraph route via the Persian Gulf was needed. She did this job in three sections, picking up a mile of cable per hour.

Cable Enterprise sailed from her Castries station in the Caribbean in the summer of 1941 to Singapore via Pernambuco, Rio de Janeiro, Cape Town, Mombasa and Colombo. Her West Indian crew had never been further than Trinidad before and looked upon the deep-sea voyage with trepidation. She ran into a heavy gale between Rio de Janeiro and Cape Town which lasted three days, with her native crew praying and singing in high voices every night in case their psalms might save the ship. The storm blew her off course by 60 miles, but she reached Cape Town and loaded repair cable for a repair at Mombasa on the Zanzibar/Aden cable. This was also carried out in ten days of heavy weather before she departed for Colombo and Singapore and repairs in the Malacca Straits. The West Indian crew were paid off at Singapore and reached home safely, and a Malayan crew was then engaged for cable repairs in the Singapore area based on Batavia. While laying a cable between Sumatra and Java she was ordered by a warship fleeing from the Japanese to drop the cable and return to Batavia. She left Java the same afternoon for Fremantle, which she reached safely and where she was based for the rest of the war. She ended the war by being one of the first ships to enter Singapore after the liberation in August,1945 by steaming up the Straits of Malacca from Cocos Island. As in the Great War, Cocos Island station was damaged by a direct hit from a warship, this time Japanese, there were no casualties and contact was re-established with Durban the next day. The Danish cableships *Pacific* and *Store Nordiske*, owned by the Great Northern Telegraph Company, were moved out of Japanese waters one week before Pearl Harbour, and were put to work for the Allied cause in the Indian Ocean and Persian Gulf. The cableship of any of the Allies, whether naval or commercially-owned or by the Post Office or P.T.T. Dept., nearest to a reported break was expected to repair it as soon as possible as a matter of national importance.

Norseman was stationed on the Brazilian coast with a Brazilian crew on the outbreak of war, and was later stationed at Castries on St. Lucia. On 22nd March,1942 a U-boat entered Castries harbour and sank two cargo-liners at their berths, one being *Lady Nelson* of Canadian National Line and she was later raised and put back into service. All ships in the vicinity were warned of the U-boat by radio from the cable station, and shortly afterwards *Norseman*, 500 miles to the north, reported a distress message saying she was being overtaken by a submarine. The submarine was seven miles from her and gaining and radio signals were sent to San Juan for a Catalina aircraft to be sent to her aid. After an hour and a half the all-clear message was received at Castries, and the 'submarine' was later found to have been an unusual type of patrol craft ! Later in the year, U-boats laid mines in the approach channel to Castries harbour, the first mine exploding when a small American launch from the U.S. Naval Air Station at Rodney

Bay on the north of the island arrived. Minesweepers were sent from the American base at Vieux Fort on the south of the island and a dozen huge mines were exploded with impressive thunderous noises and high water plumes.

Mirror under Capt. Frank Axtell, who was awarded the OBE for bravery, spent most of the war in the Bay of Biscay and in the Mediterranean. She was based at Gibraltar from the summer of 1940 until the end of 1942, and carried out repairs over a wide area from the Canaries in the south to Madeira, the Azores and north of Lisbon. Off Cape Espichel on the Arrabida peninsula to the south of Lisbon, she was closely 'buzzed' by a Focke-wolf reconaissance aircraft, which fortunately did not drop any bombs, *Mirror* having quickly let go her grapnels and cable that she had hooked. In November,1942 she laid a cable from Gibraltar to Algiers for the North African campaign, only to have to lay it again when a heavy gale caused several ships to drag their anchors and break communications. She then restored links from Algiers to Bizerta and Malta, working in narrow swept channels between minefields. She then repaired the damaged shore ends at St. George's Bay cable house at Malta, and restored links to Syracuse at the end of the Sicilian campaign and to Brindisi in Italy later in 1943.

Mirror continued working off the East coast of Italy throughout 1944, linking Naples to Palermo and Malta, and then north from Naples to Anzio and Fiumicino, 20 miles from Rome, through dangerous minefields, with hundreds of mines having to be cut free, to lay the shore-ends on these beaches. She then set off for Corsica to repair the Ajaccio/Toulon cable after the landings in Southern France, and returned to Gibraltar via Algiers. Towards the end of 1944, she headed south from Gibraltar to Dakar, St. Vincent, Cape Verde Islands, Bathurst and Sierra Leone. She then repaired the Cape Town cable at a point 800 miles from its southern terminal and while off South Africa was given an escort of two South African naval trawlers. She refuelled and stored at Walvis Bay and returned via Takoradi, Sierra Leone and Bathurst and arrived in St. Vincent harbour, Cape Verde Islands, six days after VE-day. *Mirror* had a Spanish crew from Vigo throughout the war, and other members of the fleet had Brazilian, St. Helena, Chinese, Greek, Palestinian and Lascar crews at various times, but always with British officers.

John W. Mackay was stationed at Halifax (NS) during the early part of the war, repairing North Atlantic telegraph cables. In 1942 she was requisitioned by the Admiralty for cablelaying in the Persian Gulf and Eastern Mediterranean. Due to a severe shortage of telegraph cable one of her first duties was to cut an Italian cable off the Cape Verde Islands and recover 450 miles of their cable from a depth of 2,000 fathoms for Allied use. There was heavy U-boat activity in the area at that time, and it was a miracle she was not sunk during her three weeks slow steaming in the recovery area. In 1944/45 she was cablelaying in the Pacific for the U.S. Navy.

The '*Bullfinch*' class were completed by Swan, Hunter & Wigham Richardson Ltd on the Tyne during the war for the Admiralty, their design based on *Ariel* and *Iris*(2) completed by the same yard for H.M. Postmaster General in 1939/40. *Bullfinch* was completed in 1940 and was used for harbour defence loop cablelaying and other work during the war. On 24th June 1943 *Iris*(2) inserted the first ever submarine repeater into Anglesey/Port Erin(Isle of Man) coaxial cable laid the previous year. The repeater failed after five months but was replaced by a spare which lasted seven years. The final four members of this useful class were *Bullfrog* and *St. Margarets* completed during 1944, *Bullhead* completed during 1945, with *Bullseye* completed instead for Trinity House in 1946 as a lighthouse tender.

ST. MARGARETS of 1944

Holdfast was converted into a cablelayer from the East coast passenger liner *London*, having been requisitioned on 28th August,1939 as an examination vessel and renamed *Holdfast*. Her three-month conversion into a cablelayer/pipelayer was undertaken on the Thames starting in July,1942. During December,1942 she laid an experimental length of 2" Hais petrol pipe across the Bristol Channel from Swansea to Ilfracombe. On 12th August,1944 she began the laying of PLUTO - Pipeline under the Ocean - when the first length of pipe was laid from the Isle of Wight to the tip of the Cherbourg peninsula. *Holdfast* over the next two months laid two 3" diameter petrol pipes between Sandown(Isle of Wight)/Cherbourg; as well as eleven from Dungeness/Boulogne (9 of 3" & 2 of 2"); in addition six steel 'Hamel' pipes were laid between Dungeness/Boulogne by tugs. *Holdfast* was assisted by three other merchant ships converted during 1943/44 for the laying of 'Hais' pipe: *Algerian*, *Empire Ridley* and *Empire Baffin*, and five Thames motor barges for the laying of shore ends. Over 172 million gallons of fuel were delivered under the Channel to the fighting troops in a major contribution to the final victory.

1946 Handover of *Nordeney* as war reparations to H.M. Postmaster General renamed *Alert*(3), and also *Neptun*(1) to Britain which was converted to the commercial tanker *Thule*. *Monarch*(4) completed on the Tyne for H.M. Postmaster General.
Bullhead and *Bullfrog* sold to Cable & Wireless Ltd renamed *Electra*(2) and *Retriever*(4).

1947 Two power cables laid across the Solent to the Isle of Wight.

1948 *Chiyoda Maru* completed for Nippon T. & T., based at Tokyo.

1949 *Edward Wilshaw* completed on the Tyne for Cable & Wireless Ltd.

1950 Cable & Wireless Ltd maintains a fleet of eight cable repair ships renewing an average of 1,800 miles of cable per year.

1951 *Ampere*(3) completed in Normandy for the French Government.

1952 Transatlantic cable laid to Harbour Grace in Newfoundland was the last ever telegraph cable. *Stanley Angwin* completed on the Tyne for Cable & Wireless Ltd.

1953 *Neptune, Albert J. Meyer* enter service for the U.S. military, having lain incomplete since the end of the war.

1954 Silver Jubilee of Cable & Wireless Ltd. In their booklet 'World-Wide Communications' emphasis was laid on composite submarine cable and radio networks, with their submarine cable and radio engineers being referred to as 'telecommunications' engineers for the first time.

1955 *Ocean Layer* conversion completed at Pembroke from Hansa 'B' hull for Submarine Cables Ltd. *Recorder*(3) completed on the Tyne for Cable & Wireless Ltd.

1956 TAT1 laid by *Monarch*(4) as the first Transatlantic coaxial telephone cable.
Salernum completed at Naples for Cia Italiana Navi Cablografiche.
Ocean Layer lays five power cables across from the British Columbia mainland to Vancouver Island.

1957 *Telekabel* completed for the Norwegian Government.

1958 *Ocean Layer* cablelaying in the Indian Ocean for Cable & Wireless Ltd.

1959 *Ocean Layer* cablelaying on the Brazilian coast for Cable & Wireless Ltd. On her next assignment on 14th June in mid-Atlantic while laying part of TAT2 coaxial telephone cable she is gutted by fire and is a constructive total loss. TAT2 cablelaying completed by *Monarch*(4) with *Ampere*(3) for shore ends.

1960 *Amakusa Maru* completed for the Japanese Government.

1961 CANTAT1 coaxial telephone cable laid from U.K. to Canada as first span of the Commonwealth coaxial system.
Alert(4) completed by the Fairfield yard on the Clyde for H.M. Postmaster General.
Retriever(5) completed on the Mersey for Cable & Wireless Ltd.
Dame Caroline Haslett and *Ampere*(3) lay power cables across the English Channel.
Neptun(2) enters service at Lubeck for Norddeutsche Seekabelwerke as a dual-purpose cablelayer/bulk carrier. She is sold in 1965 to the United States Undersea Cable Corporation.
Marcel Bayard completed at Le Havre for the French Government.

1962 *Mercury,* named after the Roman messenger of the Gods, completed on the Mersey as the principal cablelayer of Cable & Wireless Ltd. Her first assignment is cablelaying in the Pacific for the COMPAC coaxial system from Canada to Fiji and Australia/New Zealand.
Retriever(5) had laid the shore ends at Sydney and Auckland in April and then at Suva in October to complete the southern section.
SCOTICE/ICECAN coaxial telephone system laid by *Alert*(4), *John W. Mackay* and *Neptun* between Scotland/Iceland/Greenland and Newfoundland.
Ingul and *Jana* are the first purpose-built large cablelayers for the Soviet bloc.

1963 *Long Lines* completed at Hamburg as the largest cablelayer in the world for A.T & T.
May: She lays TAT3 coaxial from Widemouth Bay(Cornwall) to Tuckerton(NJ) with *Alert*(4).

1964 SEACOM coaxial telephone cablelaying by *Mercury* and *Monarch*(4) in Pacific and South East Asia begins.
Cable Enterprise(2) completed on the Mersey for Cable & Wireless Ltd.
November: *Photinia* lays power cables across the Cook Strait in New Zealand.

1965 July: TAT4 coaxial laid from Tuckerton(NJ) to St. Hiliaire(France) by *Long Lines* with *Marcel Bayard* for shore-ends.
Oil rigs in Gulf of Mexico connected by coaxial telephone cable.
September: *Photinia* lays power cables between Trinidad and Tobago.

1966 *Kabel-Jau* enters service for Norddeutsche Seekabelwerke as their last cablelayer. She remains in service until 1971.
Mercury lays a Bermuda/Tortola cable with Tortola the northern terminus of the later East Caribbean microwave 'line-of'sight' radio system.

1967 *KDD Maru* completed at Shimonoseki, Japan for Kokusai Cable K.K. for international cablelaying/repair.

1968 *Northern* conversion completed as the last cable repair ship of the Great Northern Telegraph Company of Denmark.
Tsna and *Donets* are the second pair of cableships completed for the Soviet bloc.

1969 SAT1 coaxial cable laid to South Africa by *Mercury* and *John W. Mackay*.
Nordkabel completed for the Norwegian Government P.T.T.
Directeur-Generaal Bast completed for Netherlands Government P.T.T.

1970 TAT5 coaxial cable laid from Green Hill (RI) to Conil(Spain) by *Long Lines*.
Monarch(4) purchased by Cable & Wireless Ltd and converted into a cable repair ship based at Bermuda and renamed *Sentinel*(2).

1971 1st January: Porthcurno Cable Station had closed at midnight, the traditional hub of British submarine cables was turned into an Engineering College. It has since been turned into a museum open to the public.
CANBER coaxial system laid by *Mercury* between Nova Scotia and Bermuda.

1972 *Mercury* lays Italy/Algeria and Spain/Canaries coaxial telephone cables.

1973 CANTAT2 Transatlantic coaxial telephone cable laid by *Mercury*.
BRACAN coaxial telephone cable laid by *Mercury* between Gran Canaria and Pernambuco.
All submarine telegraph cable now obsolete and withdrawn.

1974 Cable & Wireless Ltd and International Aeradio Ltd form Energy Communications Ltd to provide offshore telecommunications services to the North Sea oilfields.

1975 *Vercors* completed at Le Havre for France Cables and Radio.

1976 TAT6 Transatlantic coaxial cable from Green Hill(RI) to St. Hiliaire (France) laid by *Long Lines* and *Vercors*.

'Pan' type Post Office cableships C.S. *Monarch*(5) and C.S. *Iris*(3) are completed at Dundee and based at the new Southampton submarine cable service base of the General Post Office.
June: *Newton* commissioned for the Royal Navy as a cablelayer/sonar propagation ship.
August: *Flexservice 1* lays first flexible flowline in North Sea oilfields.

CABLE VENTURE at Southampton, port stern chute in foreground (Author)

1977 18th April: *Cable Venture* commissioned as a principal cablelayer for Cable & Wireless Ltd after a long conversion at Immingham from the German *Neptun*.
COLUMBUS coaxial cable laid by *Cable Venture* and *Mercury* between Spain and Venezuela.

1978 *Telepaatti* completed for the Finnish Government P.T.T.

1979 2nd May: H.M. The Queen invites directors, managers and executives of all grades to Buckingham Palace to celebrate the Golden Jubilee of Cable & Wireless Ltd
Flexservice 2 completed as first new flexible flowline layer for the North Sea oilfields.

1980 *Emba* completed for shallow water cablelaying in Northern Arctic waters of Russia.

1981 *Setun* completed for shallow water cablelaying in the Caspian Sea for Russia.

1982 TAT7 Transatlantic coaxial telephone cable laid.
Flexservice 3 completed as a large flexible flowline layer for North Sea oilfields.

1983 March: Cable & Wireless (Marine) Ltd set-up as a separate cablelaying subsidiary.
Sisters *Leon Thevenin* and *Raymond Croze* completed in France as cable repair ships, based at Brest and Toulon respectively.
December: A large flexible flowline layer completed under the British flag for the North Sea oilfields as *ITM Venturer* for ITM Offshore Ltd of Middlesbrough.
Cableships and cable assets of the General Post Office transferred to BT Marine Ltd.

1984 *Pacific Guardian* completed by Swan Hunter Shipbuilders Ltd as a cable repair ship for Cable & Wireless(Marine) Ltd and based at Suva in Fiji.

PACIFIC GUARDIAN of 1984 (Swan Hunter Shipbuilders Ltd)

1985 OPTICAN experimental optic fibre cable laid between Tenerife and Gran Canaria.
ITM Installer is commissioned by ITM Offshore Ltd for work in the North Sea oilfields.

1986 Summer: Last coaxial cable laid between India and United Arab Emirates.
 Autumn: First fibre optic cable laid between U.K. and Belgium by *Alert*(4).
 Cable Protector is commissioned by Cable & Wireless(Marine) Ltd after conversion from an oil rig supply vessel (ORSV) for route clearance and shore end work.
The dominant Japanese telecomms carrier, Nippon Telegraph &Telephone (NTT), is privatised and allowed to compete for submarine cablelaying contracts alongside Kokusai Cableship Company of K.D.D.

1987 TAT8 is first optic fibre Transatlantic cable.
TPC-3 is first fibre optic Pacific cable between U.S.A./Japan.

1988 The first privately-funded Transatlantic optical fibre cable PTAT laid by *Mercury* and *Cable Venture* with extension from New York to Bermuda.
Atlantida is the first new telecomms cablelayer for Spain. She also works on contract in the North Sea oilfields.

A wet launch day is said to be a good omen for the future employment of a ship. SIR ERIC SHARP is receiving a wet baptism at the Wallsend yard of Swan Hunter Shipbuilders Ltd on 25th October,1988 (Author).

ATLANTIDA loading flexible flowline at the former Walker Naval Yard, Newcastle (Author)

1989 March: The new Cable & Wireless(Marine) Ltd cable repair ship *Sir Eric Sharp* arrives to take up duty at Hamilton, Bermuda as guardship for PTAT and all other Transatlantic cables. She had been completed at the Wallsend yard of Swan Hunter Shipbuilders Ltd at the beginning of the year.

1990 The first new cablelayer for the United Arab Emirates is completed as *Etisalat*.
Discovery is completed under the Belgian flag as a flexible flowine layer and oil well maintenance ship for the North Sea oilfields.

1991 A large advanced cablelayer/cable repair ship is completed for BT Marine Ltd as C.S. *Sovereign* by Van de Giessen de Noord in Holland.
Three new large cable repair ships commission or complete construction at Singapore as *Global Sentinel, Global Link* and *Global Mariner* for the American fleet of A.T. & T.
They are based at Baltimore.

1992 Northern Contractors International Ltd formed by Cable & Wireless(Marine) Ltd, Ugland Offshore, and Coflexip Stena Offshore to provide submarine telecomms services across the North Sea oilfields as well as specialist oil-related work.
Seaspread begins a long Pacific maintenance contract at Victoria(BC) for Cable & Wireless (Marine) Ltd after conversion from an oil installations maintenance ship.
Teneo commissioned as a second cablelayer for Spain.

1993 TAT10/TAT11 Transatlantic fibre optic cable system laid.
TPC-4 North America/Japan fibre optic cable system laid.
C.S. *Nexus* completes conversion at Birkenhead into a cablelayer from a drillship. She is owned by James Fisher & Sons Ltd, Barrow and on long-term contract to BT Marine Ltd.

1994 September: *Asean Restorer* completed at Helsinki for Asean Cableship as a repair ship based at Singapore working in South East Asian and Indian Ocean waters.

Sunrise 2000 conversion into a flexible flowline layer completed for Coflexip Stena Offshore (C.S.O.). She later increases her depth ability to over 2,000 metres.

1995 January: BT Marine Ltd and all of its submarine cable assets and cableships purchased by Cable & Wireless(Marine) Ltd for around £40M.
March: A second oil rig supply vessel conversion joins the fleet as *Cable Installer,* her maiden lay being eight Northern segments of the Brazilian domestic system.
September: Flagship of the enlarged Cable & Wireless(Marine) Ltd fleet joins from a Helsinki shipyard as *Cable Innovator.* She is destined to lay many optical fibre systems globally as well as to show the flag for Cable & Wireless PLC around the world.
November: East Caribbean Fibre System (ECFS) completes laying by *Cable Innovator* and *Mercury,* this is the latter's last assignment after 33 years cablelaying.
Another oil rig supply vessel conversion to cablelayer is completed, this time for the American cablelaying fleet of A.T. & T. as *Coastal Connector.*

1996 Asia Pacific Cable (APC) network laid between Taiwan/Hong Kong/Singapore/Indonesia/ Malaysia/Thailand and Philippines by *Cable Innovator.*
Teliri is completed as a large new cablelayer for the Italian fleet.

1997 FLAG optical fibre system laid. Two-thirds is laid by *Cable Innovator* between Palermo (Sicily) and Mara(Japan).
Tyco Submarine Systems Ltd takes over A.T & T. Submarine Systems Inc and its submarine cable manufacturing arm. Tyco fleet also includes *Dock Express 20* on charter from Dockwise of Holland and she loads cable at the Portsmouth(New Hampshire) factory of Tyco for world-wide cablelaying.
October: Second cablerepair ship to be based at Manila as *Cable Retriever* is completed, an exact sister of *Asean Restorer.*
9th November: Final splice of the Gemini South Transatlantic optic cable by *Cable Innovator* and *Cable Venture,* this being the latter's last assignment in 20 years of cablelaying for Cable & Wireless(Marine) Ltd and a career of 35 years in submarine cable.
Seaway Eagle completed as a full cablelayer for Stolt Comex Seaways A/S for oilfield work. Fleetmates *Seaway Falcon* and *Seaway Condor* can lay rigid or flexible oil flowlines.

1998 Japan Information Highway (JIH) encircles Japan and laid by *Cable Innovator* and *C.S. Nexus.*
Agile completes her conversion in Canada to a cablelayer from a Russian Navy heavy-lift ship for charter to Cable & Wireless(Marine) Ltd. A sister completes a similar conversion in Romania and Holland as *Tyco Provider* for Tyco.
27th July: Final splice in Gemini North Transatlantic optic by *Agile* and *Maersk Defender.*
Korea Telecomms commission a large new cablelayer in *Segero.*
Spain gains a third cablelayer after the conversion of a ro-ro into *Iberus* at Vigo.
1998/99 Americas II system laid from U.S.A./Caribbean/South America by *Cable Installer.*

1999 Southern Cross optical system laid by *Cable Innovator* from Australia/New Zealand/ Hawaii.
June: Global Crossing Inc. completes takeover of Cable & Wireless Global Marine Ltd and all of its cableships, submersibles and barges for £550M to form Global Marine Systems Ltd of Chelmsford.

December: *Bold Endeavour* joins this new Global Marine Systems Ltd fleet on completion at the yard of Van de Giessen de Noord in Holland. Four more conversions with *'Wave'* names are underway at North-East coast shipyards for this fleet, which can now undertake new global cablelaying systems for the booming data traffic of the Internet, as well as undertake all of the former service contracts of Cable & Wireless Global Marine Ltd.

2000 February: *Bold Endurance* completes a conversion in Korea to a cablelayer from a Russian heavy-lift ship, she will work in the Far East for Global Marine Systems Ltd and is a near sister of *Agile* and *Tyco Provider*.

March: *Heimdal* enters service after conversion from a ro-ro in Denmark, she will work on charter to Alcatel Submarine Networks.

May: *Wave Alert*, the last of the four conversions at North-East coast shipyards, completes her conversion from an oil rig suply vessel.

June: Two ro-ros begin conversion at Rijeka into cablelayers for General Dynamics,U.S.A.

July: *Viking Lady* completes conversion at Cadiz into a cablelayer for Eidesvik A/S, Norway

GREAT BRITAIN.
I. COMMERCIAL CABLESHIPS.

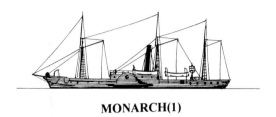

MONARCH(1)

GB1. MONARCH(1)   512 grt   156.2 x 19.7 x 14.5
E Paddle
1830 - Completed at Thornton-on-Tees.
1853 - Acquired by International Telegraph Company. First used to lay four separate cables between Orfordness and Scheveningen in May, June & September,1853 and September,1854.
1854 - Transfer to Electric & International Telegraph Company to lay cables across the Firth of Forth, Firth of Tay and Keyhaven/Hurst Castle/Isle of Wight to connect to Queen Victoria's residence, Osborne House.
1855 - Portpatrick/Donaghadee   (R.S. Newall & Co.)
1859/60 - Repairs to Weymouth/Channel Islands cables.
1860/70 - Repairs to cables owned by Electric & International Telegraph Company, Submarine Telegraph Company, British & Irish Magnetic Telegraph Company as well as for cable manufacturers.
1870 - Taken over by G.P.O. for one cable lay between Port Kale/Donaghadee, relegated to a coal hulk in the same year.

GB2. CAROLINE   526grt   153.8 x 28.2 x 15.1
E Compound , single screw.
1853 - Completed by John Scott Russell & Co., London.
1865 - Acquired by W.T. Henley's Telegraph Works Company and converted for cable work. First used for Valentia shore-end of Anglo-American Transatlantic cable.
1869 - Sweden/Russia   (Gt. Northern Telegraph Co.)
1870 - Jersey/Guernsey/Alderney   (G.P.O.)
1871 - Orkney/Shetland   (G.P.O.)
1870/80 - Assisted with shore ends for cables laid by *La Plata* and *Africa* also owned by Henley, and also frequently chartered to the G.P.O. up to 1880.
1879 - Chartered for Caribbean work by the West India & Panama Telegraph Company.
1881 - Sold for commercial use and sunk by collision in 2.1893.

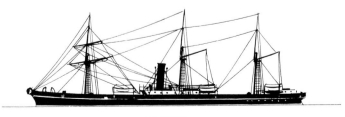

HAWK

GB3. HAWK 732 grt　　　241.8 x 28.1 x 15.1
E Compound, single screw.
CT (1), **BS** (1), **SS** (1)
1864 - Completed at Renfrew and acquired by Telcon in 1866 for conversion to cablelaying and repairing.
1869 - Assisted with first French Atlantic cable between Brest & St. Pierre with a branch to Cape Cod(Mass.)
1870 - Assisted *Great Eastern, Chiltern, Hibernia* & the chartered *William Cory* on the British Indian expedition between Bombay/Aden/Suez.
1870 - Sold to Anglo-Mediterranean Telegraph Company and laid a duplicate Malta/Sicily cable and a further cable across the Messina Straits.
1871 - Samos/Scala Nuova and Aevali/Mytilene　　　　　　(Turkish Govt.)
1871 - Canea/Rettimo/Candia/Sitia/Rhodes/Chios/Chesme　(Turkish Govt.)
1872 - Transferred to Eastern Telegraph Company and used as a repair ship in the Mediterranean until she was wrecked in 1877.

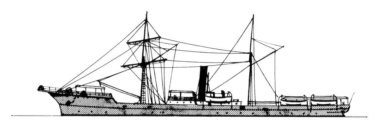

CHILTERN

GB4. CHILTERN　　　　1391 grt　　　262.0 x 31.3 x 22.6
E Compound, single screw
CT (2), **BS** (2), **SS** (1).
1866 - Completed by William Denny & Co., Dumbarton and acquired in 1867 by Telcon and fitted out for cable work.
1868 - Placentia (NFL) Transatlantic cable
1868 - Anglo-Mediterranean Telegraph Co. cables
1869 - Brest/St. Pierre
1870 - British Indian expedition
1870 - Anglo-Mediterranean Telegraph Co. cables
1870 - Sold to British Indian Submarine Telegraph Co. and assisted *Great Eastern* along with *Hawk, Hibernia* and the chartered *William Cory* on Bombay/Aden/Suez, coming south from Suez with cable from the Egyptian end to meet *Hibernia* coming from Aden off Daedalus.
1871 - Transferred to the Eastern Telegraph Company and used throughout Mediterranean.
1875 - Present at the bombardment of Alexandria and acted as a terminal station after the cables had been cut ashore.
1876/90 - Used in the Red Sea.
1890 - Fitted with new cable machinery by Johnson & Phillips.
c1900 - Sank after collision with *Mirror*(1), raised and returned to service.
1.1902 - Sold to Rudolf Neugebauer & Co. and towed to Hamburg for scrapping.

INVESTIGATOR

GB5. INVESTIGATOR   700 grt   204.4 x 28.8 x 16.2
E Compound, single screw.
CT (1), **BS** (1), **SS** (1).
1854 - Completed at Newcastle.
1868 - Purchased by Telcon and fitted out for cablelaying.
1871 - Sold to British-Australian Telegraph Co. as a repair ship.
1873 - Transferred to Eastern Ext., Australasian & China Telegraph Co.
1875 - Transferred to West India & Panama Telegraph Co.
1879 - Boiler explosion at St. Thomas, Leeward Islands and broken up.

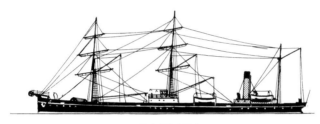

LA PLATA

GB6. LA PLATA   1218 grt   249.9 x 30.5 x 21.9
E Compound, single screw.
CT (4), **BS** (1), **SS** (1).
1862 - Completed as *Zarah* by Palmers Bros. & Co. Ltd, Jarrow as a collier.
1868 - Purchased by W.T. Henley's Telegraph Works Company and fitted out for cable work.
1868 - Denmark/Libau   (Gt. Northern Telegraph Co.)
1869 - Norway/England   (Gt. Northern Telegraph Co.)
1870 - Bona/Malta   (Marseilles,Algiers & Malta Telegraph)
1871 - Borkum/Lowestoft   (German Union Telegraph Co.)
1871 - Gibraltar/Vila Real   (Falmouth,Gibraltar & Malta Telegraph Co.)
1873 - Cuxhaven/Heligoland   (Hamburg & Heligoland Telegraph Co.)
1873 - France/Denmark   (Gt. Northern Telegraph. Co.)
1874 - Constantinople/Odessa   (Black Sea Telegraph Co.)
29.11.1874 - Lost whilst on charter to Siemens Bros. to lay a London/Buenos Aires cable.

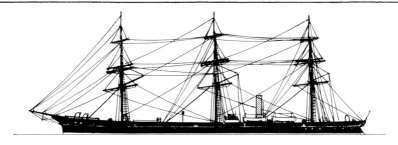

HIBERNIA

GB7. HIBERNIA   3183 grt   360.5 x 40.4 x 29.3
E Compound, single screw.
CT (3), **BS** (1), **SS** (1).
1861 - Completed by Palmers Shipbuilding & Ironworks, Jarrow as the twin-funnelled *Leinster* for Galway Line.
1869 - Purchased by Telcon from E. Bates & Company, Liverpool and fitted out for cable work, forward funnel removed.
1870 - British Indian expedition assisting *Great Eastern* on Bombay/Aden/Suez cables.
1870 - Malta/Gibraltar/Lisbon(Carcavelos)/Porthcurno.
1870 - Singapore/Djakarta link of London/Australia cable.
1871 - Port Darwin/Banjoewangie for last connection of London/Australia cable.
1876 - Botany Bay/Nelson (NZ)
30.10.1877 - Left Gravesend for Brazil to lay a further section of Para/Maranham Bay/Pernambuco cable for Western & Brazilian Telegraph Company.
21.11.1877 - Lost at Maranham Bay after grounding and breaking her back.

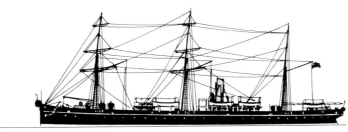

DACIA

GB8. DACIA 1856 grt   283.0 x 34.7 x 17.9
E Compound, single screw.
CT (4), **BS** (2), **SS** (1).
1867 - Completed by John Laing & Co., Sunderland for Norwood & Co., Whitby.
1870 - Acquired by India Rubber, Gutta Percha & Telegraph Works Co. and lengthened and converted into a cableship.
1870/71 - Caribbean cables   (West India & Panama Tel. Co.)
1872 - Lizard/Bilbao   (Direct Spanish Telegraph Co.)
1874 - Marseilles/Barcelona   (Direct Spanish Telegraph Co.)
1875 - Valparaiso/Lima   (West Coast of America Tel. Co.)

1880/81 - Galveston/Vera Cruz   (Mexican Telegraph Co.)

1882 - Galveston/Coatzacoalcos/Vera Cruz   (Central & Sth American Tel. Co.)

1883 - Detailed sounding of submerged peaks encountered on Cadiz/Canaries cable laid by Seine in 1882.

1883 - Senegal/Tenerife   (French Govt.)

1883/1905 - Cablelaying mostly in the Atlantic but also in the Indian Ocean and Arabian Gulf.

12.1915 - Torpedoed off Funchal harbour while diverting the German cable to South America.

GB9. INTERNATIONAL   1381 grt   240.0 x 30.1 x 17.4

E Compound, single screw.

CT (2), **BS** (1), **SS** (1)

1870 - While building for Norwood & Co.,Whitby at the yard of Richardson,Duck & Co.,Stockton she was purchased on the stocks by the India Rubber, Gutta Percha & Telegraph Works Co. and converted to a cableship.

1870 - Dartmouth/Guernsey/Jersey   (G.P.O.)

1871 - Marseilles/Algiers   (French Govt.)

1871 - Caribbean cables   (West India & Panama Tel. Co.)

1881 - Galveston/Vera Cruz   (Mexican Tel. Co.)

1883 - Senegal/Tenerife   (French Govt.)

1883/99 - Cablelaying in the Atlantic & Indian Oceans and Arabian Gulf.

1899 - Wrecked at Beachy Head while under tow to a French scrapyard.

GB10. SUFFOLK   695 grt   257.5 x 28.1 x 19.4

E Compound, twin screw.

CT (1), **BS** (1)

1866 - Completed at Port Glasgow.

1870 - Purchased by West India & Panama Telegraph Company and converted to help *Dacia* lay Cuban coastal cables and Cuba/Jamaica, Jamaica/Panama cables.

1871 - Kingston/San Juan/St. Thomas/St. Kitts/Antigua/Guadeloupe/Dominica/Martinique/St. Lucia/St. Vincent/Barbados/Grenada/Trinidad/Demerara   (West India & Panama Tel.Co.)

1873 - Sold to International Ocean Telegraph Company, renamed *Professor Morse* as a repair ship for the Western Union Atlantic cables as well as the Havana cables.

1883 - Wrecked on Block Island, Rhode Island whilst returning from a repair.

GB11. ROBERT LOWE   832 grt   201.7 x 29.3 x 16.8

E Compound, single screw.

CT (2), **BS** (2)

1870 - Completed by Palmers Shipbuilding & Ironworks Ltd, Jarrow for Anglo-American Telegraph Company in joint ownership with the French Atlantic Telegraph Company for repairs in Newfoundland waters to Transatlantic cables owned by both companies.

1873 - Wrecked on the Newfoundland coast whilst carrying out a repair.

AGNES

GB12. AGNES   781 grt   200.0 x 29.0 x 16.7
E Compound, single screw.
CT (2), **BS** (2).
1870 - Purchased by Telcon while completing at the yard of Backhouse & Co., Middlesbrough and fitted out for cablelaying.
1870 - Ionian Sea & Aegean Sea cables   (Greek Govt. & Anglo-Med. Tel. Co.)
1871 - Sold to British-Indian Extension Tel. Co. as a repair ship.
1873 - Transferred to the Eastern Extension, Australasian & China Tel. Co., based at Singapore as a repair ship.
1886 - Sold to T. Rodenacker, Danzig for commercial trading.
1901 - Sold for breaking up.

GB13. AFRICA   2279 grt   308.0 x 37.7 x 27.8
E Compound, single screw.
CT (4), **BS** (2), **SS** (1).
1869 - Completed by Robert Napier & Co. Ltd, Glasgow.
1871 - Purchased by W.T. Henley's Telegraph Works Co. & fitted out for cablelaying.
1871 - Vladivostock/Nagasaki/Shanghai/Hong Kong(Gt. Northern Tel. Co.)
1873 - Denmark/France; Denmark/Sweden   (Gt. Northern Tel. Co.)
1873 - Duplicate Denmark/England   (Gt. Northern Tel. Co.)
1873 - Straits of Messina, 2 cables   (Eastern Tel. Co.)
1873 - Porthcurno/Vigo/Lisbon   (Telcon)
1874 - Alexandria/Crete/Greece/Italy/Sicily (Telcon)
1874 - Repaired Carcavelos/Madeira cable of 1873
1874 - Sold to French owners.
1886 - Broken up.

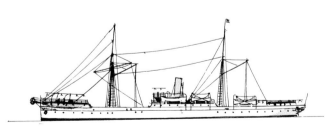

GREAT NORTHERN

GB14. GREAT NORTHERN   1422 grt   240.0 x 32.3 x 23.9

E Compound, single screw.

CT (4), **BS** (2).

1870 - Completed by Denton Gray & Co., West Hartlepool.

1871 - Purchased by Hooper's Telegraph Works Co. Ltd & fitted out for cablelaying.

1871 - Vladivostock/Nagasaki/Shanghai/Hong Kong(Gt. Northern Tel. Co.)

1875 - Batabano/Cienfuegos/Santiago (Cuba)   (West India & Panama Tel. Co.)

1878 - Alexandria/Larnaca   (Eastern Tel. Co.)

1878 - Lemnos/Salonika   (Eastern Tel. Co.)

1879 - Purchased by Eastern & South African Tel. Co. as a repair ship based at Zanzibar.

1892 - Fitted with new cable winches during a refit in the U.K.

1897 - Vigo/Gibraltar   (Eastern Tel. Co.)

5.12.1902 - Ashore on Fungu Ghawamba reef while returning to Zanzibar from Bawe Island.
Total loss but cable gear salvaged before wrecked.

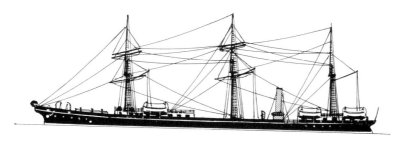

EDINBURGH

GB15. EDINBURGH   2315 grt   300.5 x 39.8 x 25.8

E Compound, single screw.

CT (4), **BS** (2), **SS** (1).

1855 - Completed by Tod & Co., Glasgow for E. Bates & Co., Liverpool.

1870 - Chartered by Telcon for two years & fitted with cable machinery.

1870 - Malta/Carcavelos/Porthcurno

1871 - Banjoewangie/Port Darwin, final London/Australia connection.

1872 - Purchased by Telcon.

1875 - Sold to Eastern Extension, Australasian & China Telegraph Co.

1879 - Purchased back by Telcon.

1880 - Last used as a cablelayer, sold for further trading renamed *Amsterdam*, subsequently
sold & renamed *Edinburgh* again.

1893 - Broken up.

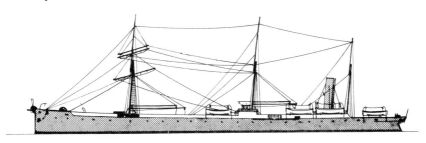

HOOPER

GB16. HOOPER   4935 grt   338.2 x 55.0 x 34.6
E Compound, single screw.
CT (3), **BS** (2), **SS** (1).
1873 - Completed by Charles Mitchell & Co., Newcastle for Hooper's Telegraph Works Ltd.
1873 - Brazilian cable from Para/Maranham Bay/Ceara/Pernambuco/Bahia/Rio de Janeiro
                                        (Western & Brazilian Telegraph Co.)
1875 - St. Croix/St. Thomas   (West India & Panama Tel. Co.)
1881 - Sold to India Rubber, Gutta Percha & Telegraph Works Co. renamed *Silvertown*.
New boilers fitted and employed in South American waters, being of great use in sending news
back to Europe during the War of the Pacific with Chile the victor.
1883/90 - West African cables   (Spanish National Tel. Co.)
1883/90 - West African cables   (African Direct Tel. Co.)
1883/90 - West African cables   (West Africa Tel. Co.)
1889/90 - Mossamedes/Angola   (Eastern & Sth. African Tel. Co.)
1890 - San Francisco/Honolulu cable, returned to Europe with cargo of grain.
1890/1916 - Worldwide cablelaying for the India Rubber,Gutta Percha & Telegraph Works.
When not cablelaying, she had periodic use as a cargo carrier
1916 - Sold to Anglo-American Oil Co. Ltd and fitted with cylindrical oil tanks.
1924 - Sold to Cie Venture-Weir S.A.,France renamed *Francunion II*
1927 - Oil storage hulk and later a coal hulk at Algiers.
1936 - Broken up in Holland.

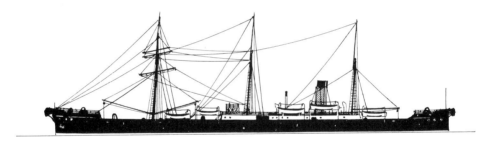

FARADAY(1)

GB17. FARADAY(1)   5052 grt   360.38 x 52.25 x 39.6
E Compound, twin screw, bow rudder.
CT (3), **BS** (2), **SS** (1)
1874 - Completed by Charles Mitchell & Co., Newcastle for Siemens Bros. Her unique hull
form was nearly identical at bow and stern, and her bow and stern sheaves were of a unique,
swivelling type. Her endurance was three months at sea, and she had a long cablelaying career
spanning 50 years and laying 50,000 n.m. of cable :-
5.1874 - Rye Beach(U.S.A.)/Tor Bay(Nova Scotia)/Ballinskelly(Eire) (Direct U.S. Cable Co)
1879 - Brest/St. Pierre   (P.-Q. Cable Company)
1881 - Cornwall/Canso(Nova Scotia) 2 cables   (Western Union Tel. Co.)
1884 - Dover Bay(Nova Scotia)/Waterville(Eire)/Weston/Le Havre (Commercial Cable Co.)
1890 - Punta Rassa/Sanibel/Key West (Fa)   (Western Union Tel.Co.)
1890 - St. Croix/St. Lucia,St.Lucia/Grenada,Grenada/Trinidad   (Direct West India Co.)
1891 - Bacton/Emden   (U.K.G.P.O.)
1894 - Dover Bay(Nova Scotia)/Waterville(Eire)/Weston/Le Havre (Commercial Cable Co.)
1895 - Galveston/Coatzacoalcos   (Mexican Tel. Co.)

1895/96 - Amazon river cable	(Amazon Tel. Co.)
1900 - Nova Scotia/Horta(Azores)/Waterville(Eire)	(Commercial Cable Co.)
1905 - Galveston/Coatzacoalcos	(Mexican Tel. Co.)
1906 - Valparaiso/Iquique/Chorillos (Lima)	(Central & Sth American)

1909 - Partially reconstructed during overhaul.

1909 - Flinders(Victoria)/Port Dalrymple(Australia)	(Australian Govt.)
1910 - Newbiggin/Arendal	(Norwegian Govt.)
1913 - Dutch East Indies cables	(Neth E.Indies Govt.)

1915 - Diverted two Atlantic cables into Newfoundland for Western Union Tel. Co.

1916 - Japanese coastal cables	(Japanese Govt.)
1918 - Murmansk/Archangel	(Gt. Northern Tel. Co.)
1920 - Colon(Panama)/Cartagena(Colombia)	(All America Cables)
1920 - San Elena/Chorillos & Cuba/Puerto Rico	(All America Cables)

1924 - Sold for breaking up but her 1" thick plates defeated the breakers, who sold her for use as a coal hulk at Algiers for the Anglo-Algiers Coaling Co. renamed *Analcoal*.

1931 - Coal hulk at Gibraltar.

1941 - Naval store ship at Sierra Leone.

1950 - Broken up in South Wales.

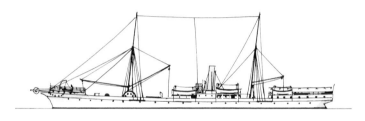

NORSEMAN(1)

GB18. NORSEMAN(1)   1368 grt   262.8 x 32.2 x 23.5

E Compound, single screw.

CT (2), **BS** (2)

1865 - Completed by Lungley & Company, London as a cargo ship.

1874 - Purchased by Western & Brazilian Telegraph Company and fitted out for cable work in South American waters by Telcon.

1875 - Duplicated Ponce/St. Croix/St. Thomas

11.1877 - Offered assistance to the grounded *Hibernia* in Maranham Bay.

1888 - Cablelaying in Plate/Parana area.

1892 - Badly damaged in a storm and sold out of the cable world.

11.1898 - Broken up.

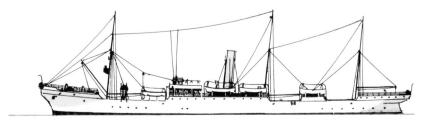

MINIA

GB19. MINIA   2061 grt   328.5 x 35.8 x 25.1
E Compound, single screw.
CT (3), **BS** (2), **SS** (1).
1866 - Completed by London & Glasgow Shipbuilding Co. Ltd, Glasgow for commercial work.
1871 - Chartered for three years by Telcon and fitted out for cable work.
1871 - China expedition including the Singapore/Hong Kong cable.
1873 - Carcavelos/Madeira assisted by *Seine*   (Brazilian Submarine Telegraph Co.)
1873 - Porthcurno/Vigo/Carcavelos assisted by *Africa* (Eastern Tel. Co.)
1874 - Jamaica/Ponce   (West India & Panama Telegraph Co.)
1874 - Sold to Anglo-American Telegraph Company, and landed the Western shore end of Hearts Content/Valentia Transatlantic cable.
1875/1912 - Used as a repair ship by Anglo-American Telegraph Company.
1912 - Leased to Western Union Telegraph Company.
1922 - Broken up.

JOHN PENDER(1)

GB20. JOHN PENDER(1)   1216 grt   246.3 x 29.2 x 20.4
E Compound, single screw.
CT (4), **BS** (2), **SS** (1)
1875 - Completed as *Saigon* by J. Scott & Company, Inverkeithing.
1877 - Purchased by Eastern Telegraph Company and fitted out for cable work.
1878 - Tenedos/Syra/Chios/Candia(Crete)   (Eastern Tel. Co.)
1878 - Antibes/Corsica   (French Govt.)
1879 - Norway/Germany   (Norwegian Govt.)
1883 - Alexandria/Port Said   (Eastern Tel. Co.)
1889 - Kalamaki/Piraeus   (Eastern Tel. Co.)
1890 - Aden/Port Sudan/Suez   (Eastern Tel. Co.)
1898 - Sold to R. Jobson & Co., West Hartlepool.
1900 - Sold to Cia Anon del Vapores Landa (Aldecoa y Urquija), Bilbao & renamed *Landa*.
12.1902 - Collision/sunk.

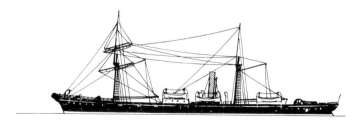

KANGAROO

GB21. KANGAROO   1773 grt   257.4 x 36.2 x 27.0
E Compound, single screw.
CT (3), **BS** (2), **SS** (1)
1853 - Completed by Hill & Co., Port Glasgow for E. Bates & Co., Liverpool.
1870 - Chartered by Telcon for Singapore/China cable   (China Submarine Tel. Co.)
1876 - Purchased by Telcon and permanently converted into a cablelayer.
1877 - Duplicate cable for Marseilles, Algiers & Malta Telegraph Co.
1882 - Malta/Tripoli   (U.K. Govt.)
1882 - Corfu/Trieste   (Eastern Tel. Co.)
1886 - Chartered by U.K. Govt. for condensing seawater into drinking water in the Sudan.
1888 - Chartered to Italian Govt. for further distilling duties in the Red Sea.
1888 - Sold to Scott & Osborne, London name unchanged.
1893 - Sold to Idarei Massousieh, Constantinople renamed *Selamet.*
1910 - Broken up.

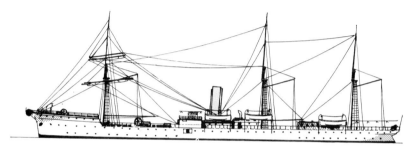

SEINE

GB22. SEINE   3553 grt   338.3 x 44.1 x 33.9
E Compound, single screw.
CT (4), **BS** (2), **SS** (1).
1859 - Completed by Thames Ironworks for Royal Mail Line as a twin-funnelled paddle steamer on West Indies service.
1872 - Converted to single screw, single funnel, and chartered to Telcon for conversion to cablelayer.
1873 - Carcavelos/Madeira   (Brazilian Submarine Tel. Co.)
1874 - Madeira/St. Vincent/Pernambuco   (Brazilian Submarine Tel. Co.)
1876 - Purchased by Telcon as a permanent cablelayer.
1879 - Duplicate of Singapore/Darwin eliminating landline in Java.
1880 - Zanzibar/Mozambique   (Eastern & Sth. African Tel. Co.)
1880 - North Sydney(NS)/St. Pierre/Roberts Bay (Anglo-American Tel. Co.)
1882 - Duplicate Carcavelos/Madeira
1882 - Duplicate Singapore/Djakarta
1883 - Direct Aden/Suez   (Eastern Extension,Australasian & China Tel.Co)
1883 - Vladivostock/Nagasaki/Shanghai/Amoy/Hong Kong (Gt. Northern Tel. Co.)
1884 - Duplicate Singapore/Saigon   (Eastern Extension,Australasian & China Tel.Co)
1885 - New engines and boilers fitted.
1888 - Java/Bali/Macassar   (Neth. East Indies Govt.)
1889 - Banjoewangie/Broome(W. Australia) (Eastern Extension,Australasian & China Tel.Co)
1896 - New York/Haiti
1905 - Broken up.

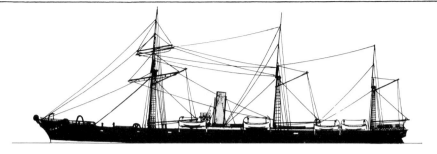

CALABRIA

GB23. CALABRIA   3231 grt   338.5 x 42.1 x 20.9

E Compound, single screw.

CT (3), **BS** (2), **SS** (1)

1857 - Completed as *Australasian* for European & Australian Royal Mail Co.,twin-funnelled

1859 - Sold to Cunard Line, Liverpool. Transatlantic services.

1869 - Renamed *Calabria*, re-engined & fore funnel removed.

1877 - Purchased by Telcon and converted for cablelaying.

1877 - Duplicate cables for Marseilles,Algiers & Malta Co., assisted by *Kangaroo*.

1879 - Maranham Bay/Pernambuco   (Western Telegraph Co.)

1879 - Less powerful compound engines installed to enable cablelaying at an economical slow speed.

1880 - Hong Kong/Philippines   (Eastern Extension.Australasian & China Tel.Co)

1880 - Zanzibar/Mozambique/Lourenco Marques (Eastern Ext.,Australasian & China Tel. Co)

1882 - Chartered by U.K. Govt. for troop carrying to South Africa and India.

1884 - Duplicate St. Vincent/Pernambuco   (Western & Brazilian Tel. Co)

1884 - Troop carrying to Egypt for U.K. Govt.

1886 - Chartered to U.K. Govt. for seawater distillation in the Sudan.

1891 - Triplicate Aden/Bombay assisted by *Scotia* (Eastern Ext.,Australasian & China Tel.Co)

1892/93 - Marseilles/Oran & Marseilles/Tunis   (French Govt.)

1896 - Germany/Vigo/Azores/New York   (German Submarine Tel.Co)

1898 - Broken up at Bolnes, Netherlands.

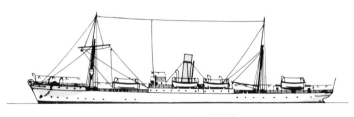

SHERARD OSBORN

GB24. SHERARD OSBORN   1429 grt   274.7 x 32.2 x 21.0

E Compound, twin screw.

CT (3), **BS** (2), **SS** (1)

4.4.1878 - Launched by Scotts' of Greenock for Eastern Extension, Australasian & China Telegraph Company and completed later in 1878.

1878/1903 - Repair ship based at Singapore for Indian Ocean & Far Eastern work.

1884 - Repairs to Singapore/Saigon/Hong Kong and Hong Kong/Tonkin and Hong Kong/Macao cables.

1885 - Bass Strait cables   (Australian Govt.)
1889 - Repairs to Saigon/Hong Kong cables.   (Eastern Ext.)
1897 - Manila/Capiz; Taburam/Escalante; Bacolod/Iloilo   (Eastern Ext.)
1897 - Penang/Malacca/Singapore   (Eastern Ext.)
1900 - Renewed Foochow/Shanghai   (Eastern Ext.)
1900 - Shanghai/Tsingtau assisted Von Podbielski   (Norddeutsche Seekabelwerke)
1901 - Woosung/Tschifu assisted Store Nordiske   (Gt. Northern Tel. Co.)
7.1903 - Repair ship based at Zanzibar.
1904 - Sold to Eastern Telegraph Company for repairs in South African waters.
1921 - Sold to C.G. Smith & Co., Durban & converted into a floating fish factory.
1937 - Sold to Italian owners renamed *Citta di Torino*.
1938 - Broken up.

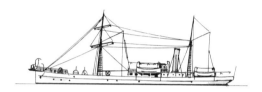

RETRIEVER(1)

GB25. RETRIEVER(1)   775 grt   180.0 x 30.3 x 15.1
E Compound, single screw.
CT (2), **BS** (2)
1878 - Completed by Cunliffe & Dunlop, Port Glasgow for West Coast of America Telegraph Company, based at Lima for repairs to Lima/Valparaiso cables.
1881 - Laid W. Coast Mexico/Salvador/Nicaragua/Costa Rica/Panama/Colombia/Ecuador & Peru cables for the Central & South American Telegraph Company.
1909 - Sold to A. Milne & Co. and converted to general cargo renamed *Clova*.
1923 - Sold & renamed *Maranon*.
7.1936 - Wrecked.

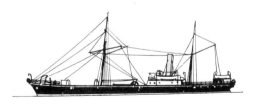

RETRIEVER(2)

GB26. RETRIEVER(2)   502 grt   178.6 x 24.2 x 12.9
E Compound, single screw.
CT (1), **BS** (2)
1879 - Completed by Blackwood & Co., Port Glasgow for Eastern Telegraph Company as a small repairing steamer for work in the Aegean.

1881 - Aegean islands cablelaying   (Greek Govt.)
17.5.1884 - Wrecked on Santorini Island, *Volta* salvaged 60 n.m. of cable from the wreck and completed the work.

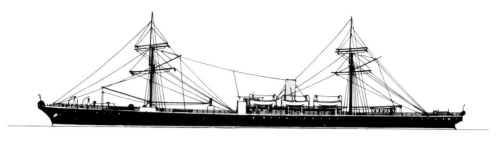

SCOTIA

GB27. SCOTIA   3871 grt   379.0 x 47.8 x 20.0
E Compound, twin screw.
CT (3), **BS** (2), **SS** (1)
1861 - Completed by R. Napier & Co., Glasgow for Cunard Line.
1863/68 - Held Blue Riband eastbound, westbound until 1867.
1875 - Laid-up at Liverpool.
1879 - Purchased by Telcon and converted for cablelaying.
1879 - Penang/Malacca/Singapore   (Eastern Ext.,Australasian & China Tel.)
1879 - Direct Singapore/Banjoewangie   (Eastern Ext.,Australasian & China Tel.)
1880 - Aden/Zanzibar   (Eastern Ext.,Australasian & China Tel.)
1880 - Valentia/Newfoundland + North Sydney/St. Pierre/Roberts Bay extension
                                             (Anglo-American Telegraph Co.)
1883 - Duplicate Vladivostock/Nagasaki/Shanghai   (Gt. Northern Telegraph Co)
1884 - Duplicate Lizard/Bilbao & Madeira/St. Vincent/Pernambuco
1887 - Duplicate Porthcurno/Carcavelos/Gibraltar (Eastern Tel. Co)
1889 - Cape Town/Nolloth/Mossamedes(Angola) (Eastern & Sth.African Tel.Co)
1890 - Duplicate Sydney/Wellington   (Eastern Ext.,Austalasian & China Tel.)
1892 - Santos/Montevideo   (Western Tel. Co)
1893 - Zanzibar/Seychelles/Mauritius   (Eastern & Sth. African Tel. Co.)
1894 - Singapore/Labuan/Hong Kong   (Eastern Ext.,Australasian & China Tel.)
1896 - Germany/Vigo/Azores/New York   (German Submarine Tel. Co.)
1896 - Explosion in her forepeak blew out her bow when 60 miles W of Eddystone.
1898 - Porthcurno/Gibraltar direct   (Eastern Tel. Co.)
1898 - Jamaica/Turks Island/Bermuda   (West India & Panama Tel. Co.)
1900 - Para/Pernambuco/Rio de Janeiro/Maldonado/Montevideo (Western Tel. Co.)
1901 - Cocos Island/Perth/Adelaide   (Eastern Ext.,Australasian & China Tel.)
1903 - Sold to Commercial Cable Company for use as a repair ship in the Pacific based Guam.
11.3.1904 - Grounded on Spanish Bank, Catalan Bank, Guam on a voyage to Honolulu and broke her back, total loss.

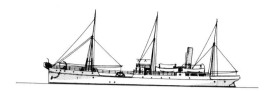

DUCHESS of MARLBOROUGH

GB28. DUCHESS of MARLBOROUGH 402 grt   172.0 x 23.0 x 12.5
E Compound, single screw.
CT (2), **BS** (2)
1874 - Completed by Barrow Shipbuilding Co., Barrow for Dublin & Glasgow Steam Packet Co. Ltd as a passenger ship.
1880 - Purchased by West India & Panama Telegraph Co. & fitted out for cable repair work in the West Indies.
1893 - Sold to Mexican Telegraph Company and renamed *Mexican*, based at Galveston for repair of Galveston/Mexico cables.
1910 - Sold to Reid(Newfoundland) Ltd renamed *Duchess of Marlborough* for commercial trading.
1913 - Wrecked off Nova Scotian coast.

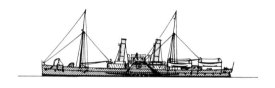

LADY CARMICHAEL

GB29. LADY CARMICHAEL   369 grt   167.8 x 25.3 x 12.1
E Paddle steamer.
CT (1), **BS** (1)
1871 - Completed by A. McMillan & Son, Dumbarton for the Submarine Telegraph Company as *Lady Carmichael* named after the wife of Chairman of the company.
1880 - Taken over by G.P.O., renamed *Alert*(1) to maintain the Channel cables.
1915 - Not fit for duty and scrapped.

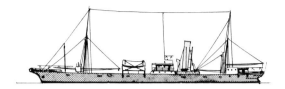

GRAPPLER

GB30. GRAPPLER   868 grt   208.5 x 29.3 x 16.2
E Compound, single screw.
CT (2), **BS** (2)
1880 - Completed by James Laing & Co., Sunderland for West India & Panama Telegraph Company, designed as a repair ship with cable machinery by Telcon.
1880/1902 - Based in the Windward Islands.
8.5.1902 - Capsized in a tidal wave after the volcanic eruption of Mount Pelee off St. Pierre, Martinique, all hands lost.

GB31. VIKING(1)   436 grt   145.0 x 23.0 x 14.5
E Compound, single screw.
CT (1), **BS** (2)
1882 - Completed by Craigie Shipyard, Dundee, designed as a cableship for the Western & Brazilian Telegraph Company with Johnson & Phillips cable machinery.
1896 - Transfer to Amazon Telegraph Company, a subsidiary, as a repair ship.
1901 - Broken up.

GB32. VOLTA   843 grt   200.2 x 29.0 x 13.8
E Compound, single screw.
CT (3), **BS** (2)
1882 - Completed by London & Glasgow Shipbuilding Co. Ltd for Eastern Telegraph Co.
1882/1884 - Ionian & Aegean Sea cablelaying   (Eastern Tel. Co. & Greek Govt.)
4.4.1887 - Stranded in Bay of Panormos on Mykonos with loss of 12 crew.

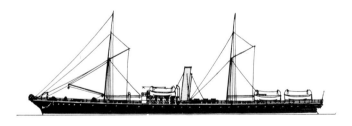

ELECTRA, MAGNETA, RECORDER(1), MIRROR(1)

GB33. ELECTRA(1)   1236 grt   237.4 x 32.1 x 16.6
E Compound, single screw, 11 knots.
CT (4), **BS** (3), **SS** (1).
1884 - Completed by Robert Napier & Sons, Glasgow for Eastern Telegraph Company. The design and location of her cable handling gear set the standard for cableships for the next one hundred years. Based at Gibraltar.

1920/22 - Malta/Alexandria assisting layer *Stephan*.
28.11.1923 - Sold for breaking up in Genoa.

GB34. MAGNETA   1236 grt   237.4 x 32.1 x 16.6
E Compound, single screw, 11 knots.
CT (4), **BS** (3), **SS** (1)
19.12.1884 - Launched by Robert Napier & Sons, Glasgow for Eastern Extension, Australasian & China Telegraph Company as an exact sister to *Electra*.
8.3.1885 - Left Gravesend for Gibraltar but lost with all hands en-route.

GB35. RECORDER(1)   1201 grt   236.8 x 32.0 x 16.5
E Compound, single screw.
CT (4), **BS** (3), **SS** (1)
1885 - Completed by Robert Napier & Sons, Glasgow for Eastern Extension,Australasian & China Telegraph Co. as a replacement for the lost *Magneta*, and sister to *Electra* in every way.
1885/1925 - Based at Singapore for full range of repairs/lays of Far Eastern cables.
15.2.1915 - Two crew wounded during mutiny of 5th Light Infantry regiment at Singapore.
1925 - Sold to Soo Chong Shipping Co. renamed *Soo Chong*.
1932 - On fire, burnt out & sank.

GB36. MIRROR(1)   1545 grt   255.7 x 34.1 x 17.6
E Compound, twin screw.
CT (4), **BS** (3), **SS** (1).
1886 - Completed by Robert Napier & Sons, Glasgow for Eastern Telegraph Company. Based in Home waters and on Gibraltar station.
1904 - Sold to Western Telegraph Company renamed *Norseman*(3), used as a repair ship.
1922 - Rio de Janeiro/Bahia cable linked into Vitoria.
1924 - Became cable hulk *Norna* in Pernambuco harbour.
1933 - Broken up.

GB37. MEDINA   286 grt   141.1 x 22.3 x 13.2
E Compound, single screw.
BS (2)
7.1867 - Completed by Charles Mitchell & Co.,Newcastle as *Prince Mohamed Tewfik*.
1884 - Purchased by Telcon and fitted out as a repair steamer, renamed *Medina*.
1885 - Repaired Fastnet/Crookhaven & Cuxhaven/Heligoland cables
1886 - Repaired Walton/Sunk cable
c1890 - Sold to H. Rasmussen, Korsor for commercial trading.
c1905 - Broken up.

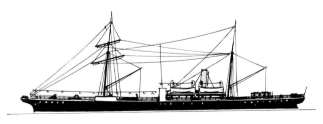

BRITANNIA

GB38. BRITANNIA   1525 grt   247.2 x 34.3 x 17.4
E Compound, twin screw.
CT (3), **BS** (2), **SS** (1)
1885 - Completed by Laird Bros.,Birkenhead for Telcon as their first specially designed cablelayer. Steel hull.
1885 - Bathurst(Gambia)/West African ports/Bonny(Nigeria) assisted by *Scotia*.
1893 - Bonny(Nigeria)/Duala(Cameroons)
1893 - Zanzibar/Seychelles/Mauritius assisted by *Scotia*.
1894 - Hearts Content/Valentia   (Anglo-American Tel.Co.)
1895 - Survey of Pacific cable route Vancouver Is./Fanning Is./Fiji/Australia & New Zealand.
1899 - Surveyed two new routes in North Atlantic, 477 soundings taken.
1900 - Germany/Azores/New York & Ireland/Azores/Nova Scotia assisted by *Anglia*.
1901 - Porthcurno/Madeira assisted by *Anglia*.
1904 - Sold to Eastern Telegraph Company, repair duties throughout Eastern network.
1907 - Renewed Barcelona/Majorca   (Spanish Govt.)
1933 - Sold to Mitchell Cotts & Co. for breaking up.

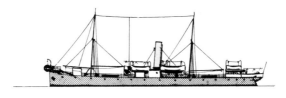

BUCCANEER

GB39. BUCCANEER   823 grt   190.0 x 28.2 x 12.8
E Compound, single screw.
CT (2), **BS** (2)
1885 - Completed by Wigham Richardson & Co.,Newcastle for India Rubber,Gutta Percha & Telegraph Works Co. as a tender to *Silvertown* ex *Hooper*.
1885/86 - A detailed sounding voyage from Cape Verde Isles to West Africa and Ascension Island under Capt. A.S. Thomson discovered an easterly flowing equatorial undercurrent beneath the westerly flowing southern ocean surface current. This important discovery was made during cablelaying with *Silvertown* and *Dacia* from Senegal/Bathurst(Gambia) /Portuguese Guinea/Konakry/Freetown/Ivory Coast/Gold Coast/Cotonou near Lagos/St. Thomas(Port.)/Loanda/Gaboon(Cameroons) for the West African Telegraph Co.
1895 - Coastal Cuba cables assisted by *Silvertown*   (Cuba Submarine Tel. Co.)
1896/1906 - North Atlantic cable work.
1914 - Wrecked.

AMBER

GB40. AMBER   1043 grt   217.5 x 31.1 x 14.3

E Triple expansion, single screw.

CT (3), **BS** (2)

1888 - Completed by Robert Napier & Sons, Glasgow for Eastern Telegraph Company.

1888/91 - Aegean islands cablelaying   (Eastern Tel. Co. & Greek Govt.)

1891/1920 - Based mostly on West African coast.

1921 - Gibraltar/Malta duplicate   (Eastern Tel. Co.)

1930 - Sold to breakers in Gibraltar.

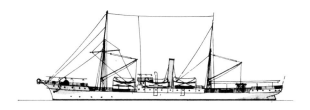

DUPLEX

GB41. DUPLEX   874 grt   214.3 x 30.2 x 17.1

E Compound, single screw.

CT (1), **BS** (2)

1872 - Completed by Charles Mitchell & Co., Newcastle as *Nentwater* for W. Dickinson & Co., Newcastle as a collier.

1893 - Purchased by Eastern & South African Telegraph Company and converted for cable repair duties renamed *Duplex*. Based on West coast of South Africa.

1913 - Sold to Cowajee, Dinshaw & Bros., India

1931 - Broken up in Italy.

GB42. NORSEMAN(2)   1123 grt   236.3 x 31.2 x 14.6

E Triple expansion, single screw.

CT (3), **BS** (2)

1893 - Completed by Ramage & Ferguson Ltd, Leith for Western & Brazilian Telegraph Company.

1899 - Transferred to Western Telegraph Company on formation.

1904 - Renamed *Norse*.

1907 - Sold out of cable world for commercial trading to A. Ballen & Co.,Callao ren *Rimac*

7.1908 - Badly damaged by fire.

1909 - Sold to Peggotini, Canepa & Schenone, Callao renamed *Monte Blanco*

1916 - Renamed *Inca*.

1917 - Sold to Cia Chilena Delquique, Valparaiso renamed *Tarapaca*.

1918 - Sold to Etchagaray Onfray y Cia, Valparaiso renamed *Coronel*.

1920 - Sold to Soc. Maritime et Commerciale de Frances renamed *San Remo*.

1922 - Sold to Giovanni Casubolo, Genoa name unchanged.

1925 - Broken up.

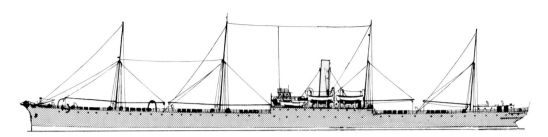

ANGLIA

GB43. ANGLIA   6514 grt   467.0 x 54.25 x 27.0
E Triple expansion by builder, twin screw.
CT (4), **BS** (2), **SS** (2).
1898 - Completed by Vickers & Maxim, Barrow for Telcon.
1899 - Gibraltar/Malta/Alexandria   (Eastern Tel. Co.)
1899/00 - Cape Town/St. Helena & Ascension/St. Vincent   (Eastern Tel. Co.)
1900 - Germany/Azores/New York with *Britannia*(2) to complete the first Transatlantic
telegraph cable for the German Government.
1900 - Waterville(Ireland/Weston-super-Mare eastern shore ends of Transatlantic cable
for the Commercial Cable Company.
1901 - Porthcurno/Madeira/St. Vincent   (Eastern Tel. Co.)
1901 - Freetown/Ascension   (Eastern Tel. Co.)
1901 - Durban/Mauritius/Rodriguez/Cocos/Perth/Adelaide with *Scotia* to complete the first
telegraph cable across the Indian Ocean.   (Eastern & Sth African Tel.Co)
1.1902 - 12.1903 Fanning Is/Suva; Suva/Norfolk Island; Norfolk Island/Queensland;
Norfolk Island/Doubtless Bay(New Zealand with *Colonia* laying the long link from
Vancouver Island to Fanning Island   (Pacific Cable Board)
+ Honolulu/Midway/Guam/Manila with *Colonia*   (Commercial Pacific Cable Co)
N.B. These two years of Pacific cablelaying were well documented in diaries and scrapbooks
of the senior cablelaying officer of *Anglia*, and describe the social life of cablelaying as
well as the more technical aspects. The astounding beauty of all of the Hawaiian islands
including Oahu, and also of Midway and Guam, where there was even a golf course for
relaxation after work, comes clearly across.
1905 - Eastern shore ends of Transatlantic cable   (Commercial Cable Co.)
1906 - Sold to W. Tamplin, London name u/ch, sheaves removed & stem straightened for
commercial trading.
1907 - Sold to Archibald Curries & Co. Pty,Melbourne renamed *Itonus*.
5.1913 - Acquired with Curries fleet by British India Line,London.
16.12.1916 - Torpedoed and sunk by U38 60 miles NW by W 1/2W from Malta on a voyage
from Marseilles to Sydney(NSW) with a cargo of tiles while requisitioned, Master taken
prisoner, 5 killed.

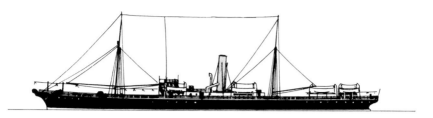

JOHN PENDER(2)

GB44. JOHN PENDER(2)   2336 grt   317.8 x 41.2 x 17.7
E Triple expansion, twin screw, 14 knots.
CT (4), **BS** (2), **SS** (1)
1900 - Completed by Robert Napier & Sons, Glasgow for Eastern Telegraph Company as a repair ship and for the laying of short telegraph cables via a stern sheave and a paying-out machine aft.

1900 - Woosung/Tschifu	(Gt. Northern Tel. Co.)
1901 - Kalamaki/Piraeus & Syra/Piraeus	(Eastern Tel. Co.)
1902 - Bathurst(Gambia)/Bissao	(West African Tel. Co.)
1902 - Lagos/Cotonou	(African Direct Tel. Co.)

1903/1920 - Mediterranean station.
1921 - Gibraltar/Malta duplicate assisting *Colonia, Amber*   (Eastern Tel. Co.)
1928 - Sold for breaking up at Antwerp.

VIKING(2) on the Amazon showing her many awnings

GB45. VIKING(2)   929 grt   207.0 x 36.0 x 13.7
E Triple expansion, single screw.
CT (3), **BS** (3), **SS** (1)
1901 - Completed by Armstrong, Whitworth & Co. Ltd, Newcastle for Amazon Telegraph Company as an Amazon river repair ship with plenty of deck awnings & cover for her crew.
1945 - Ceded to Fundacao Brasil Central on expiry of Amazon Telegraph Company concessions.
19.6.1950 - Ashore off Para and 8.1950 broke her back and sank.

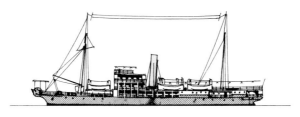

VIKING(2)

GB46. LEVANT I   141 grt   100.8 x 20.6 x 10.0
E Compound, single screw.
BS (2)
1889 - Completed by D. Macgill & Co., Irvine as trawler *W.E. Gladstone* for British Steam Trawling Company.
1900 - Purchased by Eastern Telegraph Company for cable repair work in Aegean & renamed *Levant*.
1904 - Renamed *Levant I* when *Levant II* was launched.
1906 - Laid Milo/Kimolo cable.   (Greek Govt.)
1920 - Sold to Angelides & Perris Bros., Piraeus renamed *Vrontadis*.
1931 - Sold to Vayannis & Kairaktides, Piraeus renamed *Petros Kairaktides*.
1937 - Sold to N. Mazarakis, Piraeus renamed *Kythera*.
WWII Loss.

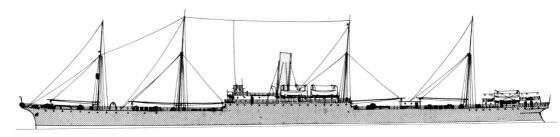

COLONIA

GB47. COLONIA   7981 grt   487.0 x 56.0 x 27.6
E Triple expansion, twin screw.
CT (4), **BS** (2), **SS** (1).
1902 - Completed by Wigham Richardson & Co. Ltd, Newcastle for Telcon.   She was built to lay in one span the very long Vancouver Island/Fanning Island stretch for the Pacific Cable Board of 3,455 n.m. and weighing 7,684 tons, the first cable of over 80,000 n.m. laid during her 26-year cablelaying career.
1.1902 - 12.1903 Vancouver Is/Fanning Is/Suva/Australia/New Zealand (Pacific Cable Board)
+ Honolulu/Midway/Guam/Manila with *Anglia*   (Commercial Pacific Cable Co)
1905 - Nova Scotia/Waterville(Ireland)/Weston-super-Mare (Commercial Cable Co.)
1906 - St. Vincent/Faya!   (Western Tel. Co.)
1907 - Durban/Mozambique   (Eastern & Sth.African Tel.Co)
1907 - New York/Cuba   (Central & Sth. American Cable)
1908 - Cadiz/Tenerife   (Spanish Govt.)
1910 - Roberts Bay/Penzance   (Anglo-American Tel. Co.)
1912 - Gibraltar/Malta/Alexandria   (Eastern Tel. Co.)
1913 - Suez/Aden/Colombo   (Eastern Ext,Australasian Tel.Co)

1913/14 - Colombo/Penang/Singapore/Hong Kong	(Eastern Ext,Australasian Tel.Co)
1914 - Freetown/Accra	(Eastern Tel. Co.)
1915 - Peterhead/Alexandrovsk	(G.P.O.)
1915 - Montevideo/Falklands Islands	(Admiralty)

1917 - Diverted German Transatlantic cables into Penzance and Halifax.

1919 - Ascension Is/Rio de Janeiro	(Western Tel. Co.)
1920 - Maranham Bay/Barbados	(Western Tel. Co.)
1920 - Miami/Barbados	(Western Union Tel. Co.)
1921 - Madras/Penang/Singapore	(Eastern Ext,Australasian Tel.Co)
1921 - Gibraltar/Malta	(Eastern Tel. Co.)

1921 - Laid first coaxial telephone cable in the world Key West/Havana (A.T. & T.)

1922 - Suez/Port Sudan/Aden/Seychelles	(Eastern Ext,Australasian Tel.Co)
1922 - Maceio/Rio de Janeiro	(Western Tel. Co.)
1922 - Pernambuco/Maranham Bay & Santos/Rio	(Western Tel. Co)
1923 - Colombo/Penang/Singapore	(Eastern Ext,Australasian Tel.Co)
1923 - New York/Azores/Le Havre	(Commercial Cable Co.)
1924 - New York/Azores	(Western Union Tel. Co.)
1924 - New York/Cuba/Colon	(All America Cables)
1924 - Malaga/Horta/Rio de Janeiro/Montevideo/B.Aires	(Italcable)
1925 - Porthcurno/Bilbao	(Eastern Tel. Co.)
1926 - Cocos Is/Cottesloe	(Eastern Ext,Australasian Tel.Co)
1927/28 - Alexandria/Port Said 2 cables	(Eastern Tel. Co.)
1928 - Larnaca/Haifa	(Eastern Tel.Co.)
1928 - Roberts Bay/Horta(Azores)	(Western Union Tel. Co.)

1928 - Sold to A/S Odd(Thor Dahl A/S), Sandefjord for conversion into a whale factory ship renamed *Torodd*.

1934 - Sold to Norske Hvalprodukter A/S(Nordstrom,Jespersen & Co.,Oslo) renamed *Sydis*.

1938 - Sold to Deutsche Olmuhlen Rohstoffe Gmbh(Hamburger Walkontor, mgr), Hamburg renamed *Sudmeer* and used in war years in the Antarctic.

10.1944 - War loss.

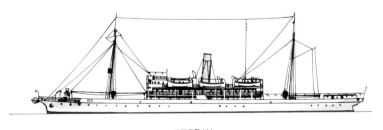

IRIS(1)

GB48. IRIS(1)   2253 grt   295.0 x 40.7 x 15.1

E Triple expansion, twin screw.

CT (4), **BS** (3), **SS** (1).

1902 - Completed by D. J. Dunlop & Co., Port Glasgow for Pacific Cable Board and based at Auckland for repair of the Pacific cables from Vancouver Island.

1912 - Diverted Norfolk Is/Doubtless Bay(NZ) cable into Auckland.

1929 - Transfer to Imperial & International Communications Ltd renamed *Recorder*(2).

1937 - Laid telephone cables across Cook Strait,New Zealand - duplicated in 1945.

1939 - Moved to Singapore station from Auckland.

12.1940 - Sailed from Bombay to the Mediterranean.

3.1941 - Cablelaying off Tobruk, then diversion of Bombay/Aden cable into muscat.

1942/45 - Based at Gibraltar, ended the war at Aden.

1947 - Extensive refit at Durban.

21.5.1952 - Arrived at Rosyth for breaking up, having been sold to BISCO for £40,000.

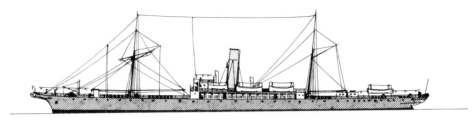

PATROL, RESTORER

GB49. PATROL   3132 grt   357.0 x 44.0 x 21.0

E Triple expansion, twin screw, 15 knots.

CT (4), **BS** (3), **SS** (1).

1903 - Completed by Swan, Hunter & Wigham Richardson Ltd for Eastern Extension, Australasian & China Telegraph Company and based at Singapore.

1903 - Balikpapan/Kwandong assisted by *Restorer*   (Neth E. Indies Govt.)

1908 - Cocos Is/Batavia   (Eastern Ext.,Australasian & China Tel.)

1929 - Continued to be based at Singapore on merger of cable interests into Cable & Wireless Ltd.

1933 - Sold for breaking up in Japan.

GB50. RESTORER   3132 grt   357.0 x 44.0 x 21.0

E Triple expansion, twin screw,15 knots.

CT (4), **BS** (3), **SS** (1).

1903 - Completed by Swan, Hunter & Wigham Richardson Ltd for Eastern Extension, Australasian & China Telegraph Company & based at Singapore.

1903 - Balikpapan/Kwandong with *Patrol*   (Neth. E. Indies Govt.)

1904 - Sold to Commercial Pacific Cable Company as a repair ship to replace the lost Scotia.

1904/1940 - Several times chartered to U.S. Govt.

1941 - Chartered by U.S. Govt. to repair the main Alaska/U.S.A. cable.

1952 - Heavy repair estimates as the ship was now 50 years of age forced her sale for breaking up.

HENRY HOLMES

GB51. HENRY HOLMES   978 grt   221.0 x 31.6 x 15.5

E Triple expansion, twin screw, 11.5 knots.

CT (3), **BS** (3), **SS** (1).

1903 - Completed by Napier & Miller Ltd, Glasgow for West India & Panama Telegraph Company, named & designed by Capt. Henry Holmes, director of the company.

8.1924 - Lost both anchors & chains in a hurricane at St. Thomas, steamed around in the harbour all night.

1928 - Similar procedure to weather another hurricane at St. Thomas.

1930 - Carried out her last voyage, and then reduced to a cable hulk on the northern shore of Castries harbour, St. Lucia.

9.1939 - Offered for sale by Cable & Wireless (West Indies) Ltd.

10.1939 - Purchased by Harold Devaux and towed a few miles south to Cul-de-Sac Bay, at entrance to valley with sugar plantations and later banana plantations.

1940/45 - Anchored near to two sugar factories and stripped of engines, boilers, pumps, lathes, drills and anything that could be used again. Then sold to a scrap dealer and insides removed, and towed further out into Bay.

c1950 - Hull gradually rotted away and sank in 8 feet of water.

1977 - Hess Oil built a oil transhipment plant at Cul-de-Sac Bay and dredged the Bay to 100 feet depth, with the old *Henry Holmes* hulk slipping into deep water.

N.B. Cable & Wireless Ltd based *Cambria* in Caribbean as a repair ship until 1933 when *Norseman*(4) took over, followed by *Retriever*(3), *Cable Enterprise* and *Lady Denison-Pender*. After WWII, *All America* was chartered as West Indies repair ship until *Electra*(2) joined the station in May,1948, in turn she was relieved by *Lady Denison-Pender* in 1958.

CORMORANT(1)

GB52. CORMORANT(1)   262 grt   133.4 x 21.7 x 11.0

E Compound, single screw.

BS (2)

1884 - Completed by Earle's Shipbuilding Co., Hull for Hewitt & Co., Hull as a coaster.

1903 - Purchased by Western Telegraph Company & fitted out for cable work.

1906 - Laid duplicate Parana river cable.

1908 - Sold to A.D. & M. Lussich, Montevideo for salvage work renamed *Salvor*.

1914 - Sold to Uruguayan Government.

1920 - Broken up.

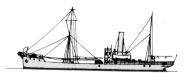

LEVANT II

GB53. LEVANT II   283 grt   138.6 x 21.6 x 11.3
E Compound, single screw.
CT (1), **BS** (2)
1904 - Completed by George Brown & Co., Greenock for Eastern Telegraph Company having been purchased on the stocks whilst building as a trawler.
1915 - Master decorated for bravery while laying a cable from Imbros to Sulva shortly after the first troop landings of Dardanelles campaign.
1916 - Lemnos/Salonika assisted by *Electra*(1)
1920 - Syra/Tenedos assisted by *Sentinel*(1)
1929 - Transfer into merged Cable & Wireless Ltd fleet.
1930/35 - Laid-up at Malta.
1935 - Sold to W.J. Parnis Ltd, Valletta renamed *Major William*.
1938 - Sold to Mrs. H.M.B. Williams renamed *Orange*.
1941 - Sold to Soc. Marseillaise de Trav., Marseilles renamed *Eissero*.
1952 - Broken up.

GB54. MAGNET   494 grt   152.0 x 26.0 x 10.0
E Triple expansion, single screw.
CT (1), **BS** (2)
1904 - Completed by Sunderland Shipbuilding Co. Ltd as coaster *Louise*, & purchased by Eastern Extension, Australasian & China Telegraph Company in same year and fitted out for cable repair work, renamed *Magnet*.
1925 - Broken up in Singapore.

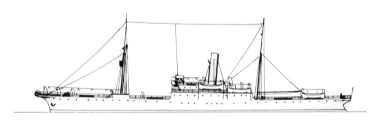

CAMBRIA

GB55. CAMBRIA   1959 grt   283.0 x 37.1 x 16.2
E Triple expansion, twin screw, 12.5 knots.
CT (3), **BS** (3), **SS** (1).
1905 Completed by Swan, Hunter & Wigham Richardson & Co. Ltd for Telcon.
1905 - Canadian shore end of Transatlantic cable   (Commercial Cable Co.)
1906 - Lerwick/Faroes/Iceland   (Gt. Northern Tel. Co.)
1910 - St. Vincent/Ascension Is/Buenos Aires   (Western Tel. Co.)
1912 - Sold to Eastern Telegraph Company.
1913 - Renewals of Brazil/Argentina   (Western Tel. Co.)
1914/1918 - Red Sea/East coast Africa operations.
1919 - Repair ship at Zanzibar for Eastern & South African Telegraph Co. - heavily damaged by storm in Mozambique Channel, repaired at Durban.
1923 - Repair ship at Cape Town for St. Helena cable - recovered Mossamedes cable.
1929 - Repair ship in West Indies until 1933.

1935 - After refit was engaged in cable renewal between Amazon & Montevideo.

1936/37 - Mediterranean work then back to Brazil.

9.1939 - Working at Dovar with naval *Lasso*.

10.1939 - Based at Plymouth for Western Approaches repairs.

1940/41 - North Atlantic operations based at Halifax (NS).

1942/45 - West Indies and South America.

8.11.1945 - Run down & sunk in Montevideo harbour by Uruguayan *Almirante Rodriguez Luis*.

SENTINEL(1), CORMORANT(2)

GB56. SENTINEL(1)   470 grt   156.7 x 25.9 x 9.7

E Triple expansion, single screw.

CT (1), **BS** (2)

1906 - Completed by Bow, McLachlan & Co. Ltd, Paisley for Eastern Telegraph Company, her sister being *Cormorant*(2) of Western Telegraph Company. They were of raised quarterdeck design and used as small repair ships.

1918 - Renamed *Sentinel II*

1920 - Syra/Tenedos assisted by *Levant II*

1922 - Sold to Western Telegraph Company after the loss of her sister.

1924 - Sold to Santiago J. Borzone, Argentina for commercial trading.

1926 - Owners became Borzone, Boggiano y Cia, Buenos Aires.

1940 - Renamed *Santa Elena* by Buenos Aires owners.

c1956 - Broken up.

GB57. CORMORANT(2)   470 grt   156.7 x 25.9 x 9.7

E Triple expansion, single screw.

CT (1), **BS** (2)

1906 - Completed by Bow, McLachlan & Co. Ltd, Paisley for Western Telegraph Company.

1922 - Wrecked off Rio Grande do Sul, Brazil. Her sister *Sentinel II* replaced her in the South American fleet of Western Telegraph Company.

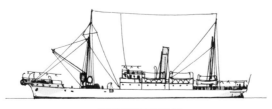

RETRIEVER(3)

GB58. RETRIEVER(3)   674 grt   190.2 x 28.3 x 15.5
E Triple expansion, single screw.
CT (3), **BS** (2).
1909 - Completed by Goole Shipbuilding & Repairing Co. Ltd for West Coast of America
Telegraph Company. Based at Callao, the port of Lima for Valparaiso/Lima cable repairs.
1929 - Joined merged Cable & Wireless Ltd fleet and saw service in West Indies, Red Sea and
Mediterranean.
1934 - Delos/Mykonos   (Greek Govt.)
6.1940 - Moved from Brazilian station to Gibraltar and cut Italy's cables to Spain.
11.4.1941 - Bombed/sunk at Piraeus. Capt. Foy and 10 out of 46 crew lost.

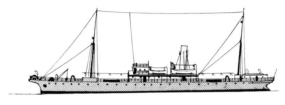

TELCONIA

GB59. TELCONIA   1013 grt   213.2 x 30.9 x 13.0
E Triple expansion, twin screw, 12 kts.
CT (3), **BS** (2), **SS** (1).
1909 - Completed by Swan, Hunter & Wigham Richardson Ltd for Telcon as a repair ship and
for connecting shore ends for the larger layers.
1910 - Penzance/Roberts Bay with Colonia   (Anglo-American Tel. Co.)
1914/18 - Diverted Borkum/Vigo cable into Sussex.
1929 - Cadiz/Arzila   (Spanish Govt.)
1932 - Broken up.

GB60. RAMOS   272 grt   123.4 x 25.1 x 7.7
E Triple expansion, twin screw.
CT (1), **BS** (2).
1912 - Completed by Napier & Miller Ltd for Amazon Telegraph Company as a shallow
draught Amazon river repair steamer with plenty of awnings and deck cover to reduce the
heat.
1945 - Transfer to Brazilian Govt. service on expiry of Amazon Telegraph Company lease.

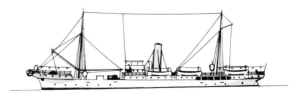

TRANSMITTER

GB61. TRANSMITTER   901 grt   208.4 x 30.1 x 16.6

E Triple expansion, single screw.

CT (3), **BS** (2).

1914 - Completed by Goole Shipbuilding & Repairing Co. Ltd for Eastern Telegraph Company.

1914 - She made three repairs to the Porthcurno/Vigo cable on her way out to West Africa.

1914 - Freetown/Accra   (African Direct Telegraph Co.)

1932 - Sold to French Govt. P.T.T. renamed Arago. Based at Dakar maintaining the French West African network of cables of Cie des Cables Sud Americains.

1944/45 - Rehabilitation of Mediterranean cables.

1946 - Sold out of cable world to Marine Nationale for clearance work in Toulon harbour.

1950 - Broken up.

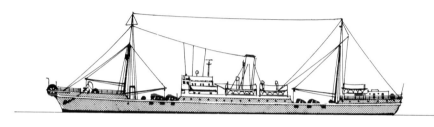

LORD KELVIN

GB62. LORD KELVIN   2641 grt   316.6 x 41.2 x 22.7

E Triple expansion, twin screw.

CT (4), **BS** (2).

1916 - Completed by Swan, Hunter & Wigham Richardson Ltd for Anglo-American Telegraph Company for cablelaying/repair under the 1911 leasing agreement with Western Union Telegraph Company, which leased all of the Anglo-American fleet. Based at Halifax(NS) for repair of North Atlantic cables.

1924 - Laid first permalloy experimental loaded cable of 120 n.m. length in a loop with both ends brought ashore at Bermuda.

1948 - Laid first flexible one-way repeater telephone cable off Bahamas for A. T. & T.

c1960 - Experimental plough trials for Western Union Telegraph Company.

1963 - Purchased by Transatlantic Cable Ltd, Bermuda after leasing agreement with Western Union had expired.

7.1966 - Sold for breaking up. She had over a 50-year career become one of the most famous cableships of all time.

7.1.1967 - Arrived La Spezia for scrapping.

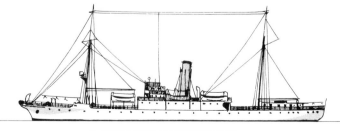

LADY DENISON-PENDER

GB63. LADY DENISON-PENDER   1984 grt   269.2 x 38.1 x 23.8

E Triple expansion, twin screw.

CT (3), **BS** (3).

1920 - Completed by Fairfield Shipbuilding & Engineering Co. Ltd, Govan for Eastern Telegraph Company. Based at Aden.

1929 - Transfer to merged Cable & Wireless Ltd fleet.

1931/38 - Based at Aden for Indian Ocean work, often visited Zanzibar.

1938/39 - Based in West Indies for repair work.

11.6.1940 - Unsuccessfully attacked at Aden by Italian bombers, moved to Atlantic station.

1.1941 - Cut the French cables Brest/Dakar and Dakar/Noronha.

1.1943 - Laid Gibraltar/Madeira cable.

3.1943 - Missed by torpedo under her stern while Convoy Commodore of Gibraltar/Freetown convoy, all other ships in the convoy sunk.

1944/45 - S. America/Pacific/N. Atlantic/Caribbean service.

1946/58 - Based at Aden and on the Brazilian coast.

1958 - Based in West Indies for repair work.

19.10.1963 - Arrived at Antwerp for breaking up.

GB64. STEPHAN   See German section

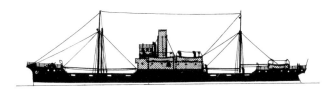

SILVERGRAY

GB65. SILVERGRAY   2456 grt   251.0 x 43.7 x 22.2

E Triple expansion, single screw.

CT (2), **BS** (2)

1920 - Completed by McDougall - Duluth Shipbuilding Co., Duluth as a molasses carrier *Julius Kessler*.

1922 - Purchased by India Rubber, Gutta Percha & Telegraph Works Co. and fitted with cable machinery in her well decks, renamed *Silvergray*.

1933 - Sold to Medway Steam Packet Co. Ltd.

c1935 - Broken up.

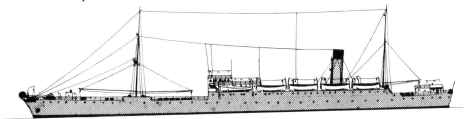

FARADAY(2)

GB66. FARADAY(2)   5533 grt   394.3 x 48.3 x 34.6

E Triple expansion, twin screw.

CT (4), **BS** (3), **SS** (1).

1923 - Completed by Palmers Shipbuilding Co. Ltd, Jarrow for Siemens Bros.

1923 - New York/Canso(NS)   (Commercial Cable Co.)

1924 - St. Vincent/Fernando Noronha/Rio de Janeiro   (Italcable)

1924 - Loaded telephone cable Aldeburgh/Domburg (G.P.O.) - duplicate 1937

1926 - Loaded telephone cable Dumpton Gap/La Panne (G.P.O.) - duplicate 1930

1926 - Balboa/San Elena   (All America Cables)

1927 - Duplicate Fanning Is/Suva   (Pacific Cable Board)

1928 - Beirut/Nabeul   (French Govt.)

1930/31 - Mostly laid-up

1932 - Loaded telephone cable St. Margarets Bay/La Panne (G.P.O.)

1935 - Bass Strait coaxial telephone cable   (Australian Govt.)

6.1937 - Anglo - Dutch coaxial telephone cables   (G.P.O.)

1937/38 - Donaghadee/Port Kale coaxial   (G.P.O.)

1937/38 - Aber Geich/Howth coaxial   (G.P.O.)

1937/38 - Dartmouth/Guernsey/Jersey coaxial   (G.P.O.)

1938 - Tunis/Beirut coaxial   (French Govt.)

1938 - Jersey/Pirou coaxial   (French Govt.)

1940 - Diversion of German cable for Allied use.

12.1940 - Loaded cable at Greenwich for cablelaying expedition.

25.3.1941 - Bombed and set on fire on a voyage Falmouth/Milford Haven at 1945 hours, crew abandoned ship, wreck drifted ashore to N of St. Anne's Head.

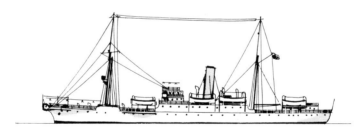

MIRROR(2), NORSEMAN(4)

GB67. MIRROR(2)   1850 grt   259.2 x 37.2 x 22.9

E Triple expansion, twin sscrew, 12 knots.

CT (3), **BS** (3).

1923 - Completed by John Brown & Co. Ltd, Clydebank for Eastern Telegraph Company. Her sişter was *Norseman*(4) from same yard, very tall masts as had all Eastern ships of this time.

1929 - Transfer to merged Cable & Wireless Ltd fleet.

6.1940 - While at Gibraltar cut Italy's cables to Spain and South America.

10.1942 - Laid Gibraltar/Algiers cable for North Africa landings

1943/44 - Based at Algiers and Naples laying cables to support advancing troops.

1945 - Repaired cables off W. Africa and in S. Atlantic.

5.1945 - At St. Vincent, Cape Verde Islands at end of war.

11.1964 - Sold for scrapping to Belgium breakers.

GB68. NORSEMAN(4)   1844 grt   259.2 x 37.2 x 22.9
E Triple expansion, twin screw, 12 knots.
CT (3), **BS** (3).
1923 - Completed by John Brown & Co. Ltd, Clydebank for Western Telegraph Company, identical in every way to *Mirror*(2). Based East coast S. America.
1929 - Transfer to merged Cable & Wireless Ltd fleet.
1933 - Stationed in West Indies for cable repair work.
6.1940 - Cut Italy's cables to Spain and S. America.
22.3.1942 - 'Scare' when 'attacked' by guboat 500 miles N of St. Lucia.
1946 - Returned to S. American station.
1956 - Renewed Rio de Janeiro/Pernambuco; Pernambuco/Bahia; Salvador/Vitoria cables.
1959 - Renewed Pernambuco/Maceio; Pernambuco/Natal cables.
12.3.1964 - Arrived Ghent for breaking up.

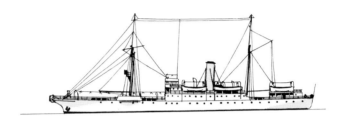

THE CABLE

GB69. THE CABLE   1534 grt   238.2 x 35.3 x 22.1
E Triple expansion, twin screw, 12.5 knots.
CT (3), **BS** (3).
10.1924 - Completed by Alexander Stephen & Sons Ltd, Glasgow for Eastern Extension, Australasian & China Telegraph Company. Based in Far East.
1929 - Transfer to merged Cable & Wireless Ltd fleet.
9.1935 - Struck an uncharted rock off Cape St. James, Saigon and sank.

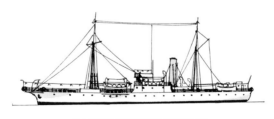

CABLE ENTERPRISE(1)

GB70. CABLE ENTERPRISE(1) 943 grt   198.9 x 30.1 x 19.4
E Triple expansion, single screw, 10.5 knots.
CT (2), **BS** (3).
1924 - Completed by A. & J. Inglis Ltd, Glasgow for Western Telegraph Company.
1924 - Connected Florianopolis & Rio Grande do Sul into main Brazilian coastal cable.
1929 - Transfer into merged Cable & Wireless Ltd fleet.
1935/37 - West Indies repair ship.

6.1941 - Sailed from Castries, St. Lucia to Singapore via Pernambuco, Rio de Janeiro, Cape Town, Mombasa and Colombo - repaired Zanzibar/Aden cable on the way.

2.1942 - While laying a Sumatra/Java cable, she was ordered into Batavia and then to Fremantle to escape the advancing Japanese.

8.1945 - Arrived at Singapore following liberation of the port.

1955 - Laid-up at Plymouth, sold to Comital S.A., Switzerland with plans to modernise her, none became a reality and she remained laid-up at Plymouth until sold to Dutch breakers, arriving in tow in New Waterway on 20.4.1960.

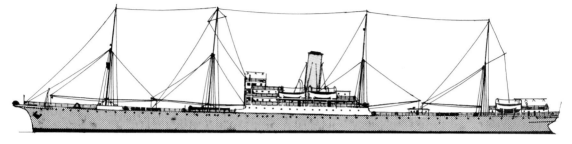

DOMINIA

GB71. DOMINIA   9273 grt   488.9 x 59.0 x 37.4

E   Triple expansion, twin screw.

CT (4), **BS** (3), **SS** (1).

1926 - Completed by Swan, Hunter & Wigham Richardson Ltd for Telcon. Maiden voyage with duplicate 'loaded' cable for Vancouver Is/Fanning Is for Pacific Cable Board, 3627 n.m. weighing 8594 tons.

1929 - Algeciras/Ceuta & Tenerife/Gran Canarias   (Spanish Govt.)
1929 - Vigo/Carcavelos   (Eastern Tel. Co.)
1930 - Willemstad/La Guayra & Willemstad/Aruba   (All America Cables)
1930 - Aruba/Maracaibo & Maracaibo/Barranquilla (All America Cables)
1930 - Lisbon/La Panne   (Italian Govt.)

1931/34 - Mostly laid-up.

1935 - Merger of Telcon and Siemens Bros cable interests required only one large layer instead of two, *Faraday*(2) being retained.

1937 - Sold to Russian Govt. & converted to general cargo renamed *Nikolai Ejov*.

1959 - Broken up in Russia.

GB72. RETRIEVER(4)   See *Bullfrog* in Section III.

GB73. ELECTRA(2)   See *Bullhead* in Section III.

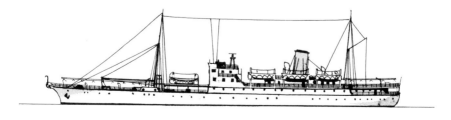

EDWARD WILSHAW, STANLEY ANGWIN

GB74. EDWARD WILSHAW   2522 grt   313.2 x 41.2 x 19.0

E Triple expansion, twin screw, 11 knots.

CT (3), **BS** (3).

1949 - Completed by Swan, Hunter & Wigham Richardson Ltd for Cable & Wireless Ltd.

1949/64 - Based in Singapore/Indian Ocean.

1965/70 - Based in Mediterranean/S. Atlantic/W. Coast of Africa.

1970/79 - Based in Australasia, Pacific & W. Coast United States.

12.12.1979 - Arrived at Vigo for breaking up.

GB75. STANLEY ANGWIN   2530 grt   318.3 x 41.2 x 19.0

E Triple expansion, twin screw, 11 knots.

CT (3), **BS** (3).

1952 - Completed by Swan, Hunter & Wigham Richardson Ltd for Cable & Wireless Ltd. Nearly identical to *Edward Wilshaw* except that one boiler was never fitted, and also additional accomodation was provided on the boat deck.

1952/55 - Based at Singapore.

1960/71 - Based in West Indies/United States/Plate/W. Coast of Africa.

1966 - Surveyed Tortola/Bermuda coaxial telephone cable route.

3.1971 - Laid-up & 16.5.1972 - arrived Antwerp for breaking up.

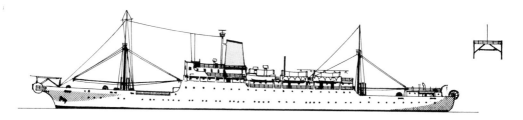

OCEAN LAYER

GB76. OCEAN LAYER   4534 grt   378.0 x 50.9 x 21.25

E Double compound & exhaust turbine.

CT (4), **BS** (3), **SS** (1).

5.1945 - Taken in prize while on stocks at Flensburger Schiffs, Germany. Hansa 'B' hull.

1948 - Completed as *Empire Frome* for Ministry of Transport.

1953 - Purchased by Submarine Cables Ltd and converted by R.S. Hayes Ltd into a cablelayer at Pembroke Dock.

1955 - Renamed *Ocean Layer* and laid Denmark/Norway coaxial telephone cable.

2.1956 - 3.1956 - Renewed Pernambuco/Bahia/Vitoria   (Cable & Wireless Ltd)

4.1956 - 10.1956 - Brit. Columbia/Vancouver Is power cables   (BICC)

12.1956 - 2.1957 - Refit.

1957 - San Francisco/Hawaii coaxial telephone   (A.T. & T.)

1957/58 - Renewal of Indian Ocean cables   (Cable & Wireless Ltd)

6.1958 - 1.1959 - Refit and then renewal work on Brazilian coast   (Cable & Wireless Ltd)

14.6.1959 - Having loaded a France/Newfoundland Transatlantic coaxial telephone cable, she caught fire while laying this approx. 450 miles W of Ushant, taken in tow by German salvage tug three days later and arrived Falmouth 21.6.1959, constructive total loss. This was one of the very few occasions when a cable was lost while in the process of being laid.

12.1959 - Broken up at Hendrik-Ido-Ambacht, Holland.

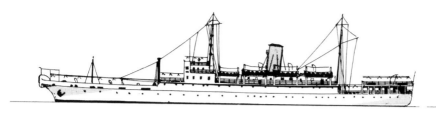

RECORDER(3)

GB77. RECORDER(3)   3430 grt   340.5 x 45.2 x 18.6
E Triple expansion, twin screw, 12 knots.
CT (3), **BS** (3). Fitted with gas turbine bow thruster, later replaced by Gill thruster.
1955 - Completed by Swan, Hunter & Wigham Richardson Ltd for Cable & Wireless Ltd.
Based at Singapore throughout her career of 30 years.
1964 - Pacific surveys for SEACOM coaxial telephone cable & shore ends at Sabah, Borneo.
She also at this time raised the obsolete Pacific telegraph cables from U.S.A./Hawaii/Guam/
Philippines route of Commercial Pacific Cable Company.
2.1985 - Still based at Singapore until replaced this month by *Retriever*(5). Broken up by the
end of 1985, probably in Far East.

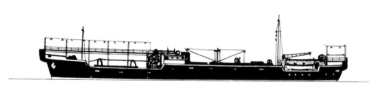

DAME CAROLINE HASLETT

GB78. DAME CAROLINE HASLETT   1777 grt   270' x 39' x 16.5'
E 8-cylinder 2SCSA oil engine by British Polar Engines Ltd, Glasgow.
CT (3), **BS** (2), **SS** (2)
2.1950 - Completed by Hall, Russell & Co. Ltd, Aberdeen as a 'flat-iron' collier for the British
Electricity Authority.
1954 - Owners became the Central Electricity Authority.
1958 - Owners became the Central Electricity Generating Board, and temporarily fitted with
cable-laying gear by Penarth Pontoon & Slipway Ltd for Anglo-French power cables under the
Channel, based at Shoreham.
1966 - Converted to a permanent cablelayer by R. & H. Green & Silley Weir Ltd, London.
1982 - Sold out of the cable world for commercial use renamed *Dame Caroline*.
6.3.1984 - Breaking-up began at South Bank, Middlesbrough.

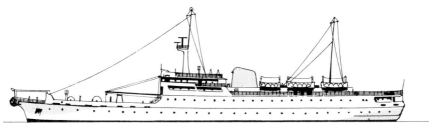

RETRIEVER(5)

GB79. RETRIEVER(5)   4218 grt   366.0 x 47.7 x 19.1
E Diesel electric propulsion by English Electric, twin screw, Voith-Schneider bow thruster later replaced by Gill thruster.
CT (3), **BS** (3), **SS** (1).
1961 - Completed by Cammell, Laird & Co. Ltd, Birkenhead for Cable & Wireless Ltd.
1961 - Manahawkin(U.S.A.)/Bermuda coaxial telephone shore ends.
1962 - Shore ends at Auckland and Sydney for COMPAC coaxial telephone cable.
1962/85 - Mostly based in the Pacific to maintain Canada/Australia telephone cables. 12 hours readiness to sail to complete repairs, several needed on Fiji/Hawaii and Port Alberni/Hawaii segments in 1982.
1983/84 - Preparatory route clearing for ANZCAN coaxial telephone cable, repositioned the Fiji sea earth and cable of Fiji/Auckland segment of COMPAC. Shore ends at Fiji for ANZCAN with cable route buoy marking, and work on Fiji/Honolulu segment.
2.1985 - Transfer as repair ship to Singapore replacing *Recorder*(3).
17.4.1995 - Arrived Alang, India for breaking up.

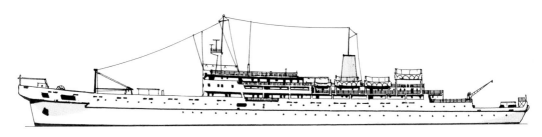

MERCURY

GB80. MERCURY   8962 grt   473.0 x 58.8 x 24.7
E Diesel-electric propulsion, twin screw, 16 knots, 8,000 mile range or 60 days.
CT (3), **BS** (2), **SS** (1).
1962 - Completed by Cammell, Laird & Co. Ltd, Birkenhead for Cable & Wireless Ltd. Named after the Roman messenger of the Gods. Master and 29 officers, 5 petty officers and 124 Spanish crew from the Vigo and La Linea areas of Spain. She and *Cable Venture ex Neptun*, which entered service after conversion in 1977, were the two big C. & W. cablelayers of the post-WWII years.
1962/63 - COMPAC Pacific coaxial telephone cablelaying.
1964/66 - SEACOM Pacific and South East Asia coaxial telephone cablelaying.
1966 - Bermuda/ Tortola, West Indies coaxial telephone cable
1968/69 - Sesimbra(Portugal)/Cape Town coaxial SAT1   (South Atlantic Cable Co)

1971 - Nova Scotia/Bermuda coaxial telephone cable(CANBER)   (C.O.T.C.)
1971 - Jamaica/Cayman Islands coaxial telephone cable   (C. & W.)
1972 - Pisa(Italy)/Algeria coaxial telephone cable   (Italian Govt.)
1972 - Spain/Canaries coaxial telephone cable   (Spanish Govt.)
1973 - Gran Canarias/Pernambuco coaxial telephone cable   (Spanish Govt.)
6.1973 - 12.1973 - CANTAT2 Widemouth Bay/Halifax(NS) coaxial   (G.P.O.)
1975 - TASMAN coaxial telephone cable   (Australian/NZ Govts.)
1975 - Cornwall/Spain coaxial telephone cable   (Spanish Govt.)
1976 - Catania(Italy)/Antalya(Turkey coaxial   (Italian Govt.)
1977 - Spain/Venezuela coaxial telephone cable   (Spanish Govt.)
1978 - Barcelona/Majorca coaxial telephone cable   (Spanish Govt.)
1980 - Based at Vigo as repair ship under Atlantic Cable Maintenance Agreement, 30 repairs carried out in North and South Atlantic during the next 5 years, including extensive refurbishment of some Transatlantic cables.
9.1982 - *Scarab* submersible used for cable burial of CANTAT2 and TAT7 cables.
1983/84 - Laying ANZCAN Pacific coaxial telephone cable with *Cable Venture*.
6.1984 - *Scarab* submersible used for TAT5 cable repair/burial.
1988/89 - Laid PTAT Transatlantic optical fibre system with *Cable Venture*.
1989/95 - Worldwide optical fibre cablelaying.
1995/96 - Laid ECFS (East Caribbean Fibre System), which replaced the East Caribbean microwave line-of-sight system of 1971; this was her final cablelaying assignment after 34 years cablelaying for Cable & Wireless Ltd.
1.5.1996 - Seriously damaged after engine room fire while laid-up at Bristol.
11.1997 - Sold to Turkish breakers and arrived Aliaga during 1.1998 for scrapping.

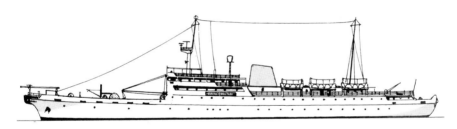

CABLE ENTERPRISE(2)

GB81. CABLE ENTERPRISE(2)   4058 grt   371.4 x 49.2 x 19.1
E Diesel-electric propulsion, twin screw, 15 knots, 6,000 mile range or 47 days, 90 crew. Bow rudder later replaced by bow thruster.
CT (3), **BS** (3), **SS** (1). 738 cu. metres coiling capacity.
1964 - Completed by Cammell, Laird & Co. Ltd, Birkenhead for Cable & Wireless Ltd.
1965 - Shore end of SEACOM coaxial at Singapore, and took up station there as guardship for North Pacific cables.
1982 - Route survey for ANZCAN coaxial off Hawaii, and shore ends of Port Alberni/Honolulu and Honolulu/Fiji segments.
1983 - Six repairs carried out to coaxial telephone cables off Hawaii.
1999- Route clearance of 1800 km of cable over 160 days for Japan Information Highway. *(re cleared old cable)*
6.1999 - Transfer to Global Marine Systems Ltd.

Scrapped 2002

GB82. SENTINEL(2)   See *Monarch*(4) in Section III.

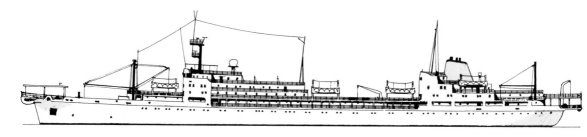

CABLE VENTURE

GB83. CABLE VENTURE   9019grt   493.9 x 61.8 x 29.5
E Diesel or diesel-electric propulsion, twin screw. Bow thruster, active rudder.
CT (4), **BS** (3), **SS** (1).
1962 - Completed by Lubecker Flenderweke A.G. as *Neptun* for Union Kabellgungs &
Schiffarts as a dual cablelayer/bulk carrier for use by Norddeutsche Seekabelwerke (q.v.)
12.1975 - Purchased by Cable & Wireless Ltd from International Marine Operations,U.S.A.
and sent to Immingham for modernisation by Humber Graving Dock & Engineering Company.
Converted into a permanent cablelayer, with a covered deck for cable operations with test
rooms and accomodation built above. Forward cable machinery modernised.
18.4.1977 - Commissioned and named *Cable Venture* by Princess Margaret and entered
service in August,1977 as the principal Cable & Wireless Ltd cablelayer.
1980 - Major refit including installation of plough and new stern chute.
1983/84 - Laid all the deep-water sections of ANZCAN telephone cable assisted by *Mercury*.
1984 - Laid Singapore/Hong Kong/Taiwan coaxial cable.
1988/89 - Laid PTAT Transatlantic optical fibre system with *Mercury*.
1989/97 - Worldwide optical fibre cablelaying.
9.11.1997 - Final splice of Gemini South system from Manasquan(U.S.A.) to Porthcurno, laid
with *Cable Innovator*, marked the end of her 20 years of cablelaying for Cable & Wireless.
3.1998 - Sold to Pounds, Portsmouth and towed from Avonmouth to Portsmouth under the
name *Able Venture*.
14.5.1998 - Arrived Alang, India for breaking up, scrap price $0.568M.

GB84. ITM VENTURER   9487 grt   128.5 x 34.8 x 5.4
E Diesel-electric. 5 Daihatsu 12-cyinder diesels linked to four electric motor and four
controllable pitch propellers, 3 thrusters.
12.1983 - Completed by Hyundai Mipo Dockyard Ltd, Ulsan for ITM Offshore Ltd,
Middlesbrough as a cablelayer/flexible pipelayer.
1987 - Sold to Stena Offshore A/B, Sweden renamed *Northern Venturer*.
1988 - Sold to Davy Normanby Ltd, Middlesbrough and continued working in North Sea
oilfields.
12.1988 - Sold to Italcable s.p.A.,Sorrento renamed *Giulio Verne* for Mediterranean cable
work based near Naples and managed by V Ships of Castellamare, tonnage now 10,617 grt.

10.8.1999 - Serious damage to engines and accomodation while loading cable at the Pirelli pier at Arco Felice, Pozzuoli near Naples. Repaired in Italy and still in service after the millennium.

GB85. SEAWAY CONDOR   6208 grt   101.94 x 19.94 x 5.5

E Diesel-electric. Six MaK 8-cylinder oil engines driving six generators connected to two electric motors & two shafts. 12 knots.

1982 - Completed by Werft Nobiskrug GmbH, Rendsburg for SCS Shipping Ltd (Stolt Comex Seaway A/S) as a diving maintenance/fire-fighting ship with three moonpools.

1984 - Converted into a flexible pipelayer/cablelayer with one 70-ton crane to load/unload lengths of pipe.

1999 - Upgraded by Cammell, Laird & Co. Ltd, Birkenhead to carry 3,000 tonnes of flexible pipe plus 8 reels on deck, lengthened by 30 metres, 60-tonne crane added plus 1600-tonne powered carousel in new mid-section and 250-tonne 'A' frame over stern. Two wide cable drums placed vertically at her stern act as sheaves to lay flexibles and umbilicals in up to 2,000 metres of water. Refit completed during 5.2000.

6.2000 - Three year contract to Petrobras in Campos Basin oilfield, Brazil to NE of Rio de Janeiro.

GB86. PACIFIC GUARDIAN   6133 grt   115.02 x 18.04 x 6.3

E Diesel-electric propulsion comprising two Ruston Vee 12-cylinder oil engines connected to 2 electric motors, 5718 bhp, 16 knots.

CT (3), **BS** (1), **SS** (1). Coiling capacity of 2620 cu. metres, additional storage for cable, ropes etc adjacent to cable tanks, linear cable engine. 40 days endurance including 6750 miles of passage at 12 knots. 76 crew + berths for cable technicians and observers.

13.6.1984 - Launched and 10.1984 completed by Swan Hunter Shipbuilders Ltd, Wallsend for Cable & Wireless Ltd.

3.1985 - After visit to London she arrived on station at Suva, Fiji to take over from *Retriever* as 'resident' repair ship under the 25-year Pacific Cable Maintenance Agreement.

6.1999 - Transfer to Global Marine Systems Ltd

2000 - On station in southern sector of the Pacific, based at Auckland or Sydney(NSW).

GB87. SIR ERIC SHARP   6141 grt   115.02 x 18.22 x 6.3

E Diesel-electric propulsion comprising two Ruston Vee 12-cylinder oil engines connected to 2 electric motors, 6000 bhp 16 knots.

CT (3), **BS** (1), **SS** (1). Coiling capacity of 1416 cu. metres or 1700 tonnes, linear cable engine aft, 2 drum engines forward. 40 days endurance including 6750 miles of passage at 12 knots. 76 crew + 11 berths for cable technicians and observers.

25.10.1988 - Launched and 1.1989 completed by Swan Hunter Shipbuilders Ltd, Wallsend for Cable & Wireless Ltd

3.1989 - Took up station at Hamilton, Bermuda as repair ship for the Atlantic section of C. & W.'s Global Digital Highway for maintenance of PTAT system, the first privately-funded Transatlantic fibre optic telecomms cable, and repair of existing coaxial cables. She was the first cableship to be designed with a permanent remotely-controlled submersible vehicle (ROV128) for buried cable maintenance tasks of below 2000 metres from sealevel. Ice strengthened, fully air-conditioned. Dynamic positioning and satellite navigation systems fitted later. Water evaporator produces 25 tons of fresh water/day.

6.1999 - Transfer to Global Marine Systems Ltd.

2000 - Still on station in Bermuda covering the Caribbean and North Atlantic sectors.

The cable deck of CABLE PROTECTOR   (Author)

GB88. CABLE PROTECTOR   1599 grt   82.2 x 17.5 x 7.0
E 2 Polar 12-cylinder oil engines by British Polar Engines Ltd; 2 controllable pitch propellers.
CT (2), **SS** (1)
1.1976 - Completed by Smith's Dock Co. Ltd, Middlesbrough as *Star Arcturus* for Star Offshore Services Ltd, Aberdeen.
1986 - Purchased by Cable & Wireless (Marine) Ltd renamed *Cable Protector*, fitted with two cable tanks and converted for cablelaying duties, working with *Cable Venture* on occasions. Cablelaying assignments included shore-end laying and route clearance.
1992 - Sold to Tuyau Shipping N.V.(Workships Contractors B.V.) renamed *Cable Carrier*, continued to work in the North Sea oilfields.
2000 - Still in service.

GB89. CABLE INSTALLER   2996/80   82.6 x 17.6 x 7.0
E 2 Ruston 12-cylinder oil engines; 2 controllable pitch propellers, 3 thrusters.
CT (2), **SS** (1), 1 cable drum engine.
2.1980 - Completed by Appledore Shipbuilders Ltd as *Star Hercules* for Star Offshore Services Ltd, Aberdeen.
7-8/1988 and 1-3/1989 - Temporarily converted for cablelaying.
1995 - Purchased by Cable & Wireless (Marine) Ltd renamed *Cable Installer* and permanently converted for cablelaying duties, 1700 tons of cable capacity, stern 'A' frame, 3 deck cranes. 50 officers & crew.
3.1996 - Conversion complete & began laying the eight Northern segments of the Brazilian domestic cable system.
1999 - AmericasII system cablelaying from U.S./Caribbean/South America.

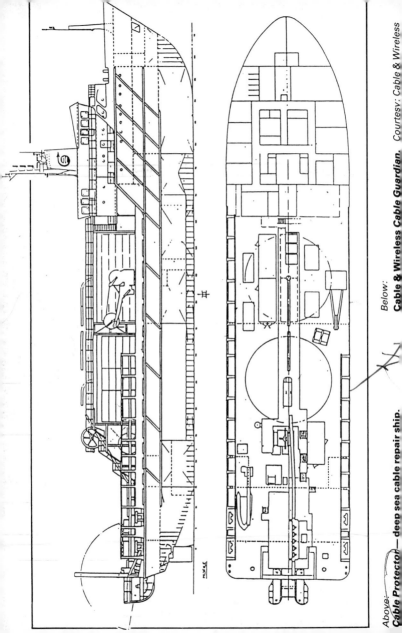

Above:
Cable Protector — deep sea cable repair ship.

Below:
Cable & Wireless Cable Guardian. Courtesy: Cable & Wireless

Name	Year	NRT	GRT	DWT	LOA	BM	DFT	SPD
La Colina (1)	1976	1,144	1,599	3,455	96	14.1	5.5	13.8
La Falda (1)	1972	1,035	1,599	3,439	100.7	14.6	5.9	16
La Hacienda (1)	1969	675	1,452	2,365	80.5	12.7	5.2	13
La Pampa (3)	1982	30,183	41,934	77,300	230	32.3	14.9	14
La Pradera (1)	1976	1,144	1,599	3,455	96	14.1	5.5	13.8
La Quinta (1)	1969	675	1,452	2,256	80.5	12.7	5.2	13
Larkfield (2)	1974	12,385	24,787	39,011	182	29	11.6	14.5
Petersfield (2)	1985	12,649	27,818	41,649	187.5	29.5	11.6	13
Princefield (2)	1974	12,385	24,787	38,325	182	29	11.6	14.5
Richfield (2)	1974	12,385	24,787	39,082	182	29.1	11.6	14.5
Silverfalcon (1)	1966	661	1,301	1,940	77.3	12.7	4.8	12
Silvermerlin (1)	1968	639	1,259	1,901	77.3	12.3	4.8	12
Summerfield (2)	1974	12,385	24,787	39,008	182	29.1	11.6	14.5
Westfield (2)	1985	12,649	27,818	41,619	187.5	29.5	12.1	13

Notes: (1) Oil and/or chemical tanker; (2) geared bulk carrier with capacity for 1,584 TEUs; (3) gearless bulk carrier.

BURMAH OIL TRADING LTD

68 Mount Street, London W1Y 5HL
Tel: (01-) 499 9533   *Telex:* 8813598

Founded in 1902, Burmah Oil expanded its activities and registered a new company (as above) in London in 1908. The company specialises in the carriage of oils, both crude and refined, on a world-wide basis.

Name	Year	NRT	GRT	DWT	LOA	BM	DFT	SPD
Burmah Endeavour	1977	183,336	231,629	457,841	378.4	68	25	16
Burmah Enterprise	1978	183,336	231,629	457,927	378.4	68	25	16

CABLE & WIRELESS (MARINE) LTD

East Saxon House, 27 Duke Street, Chelmsford, Essex CM1 1HT
Tel: (0245) 260881   *Telex:* 23181

John Pender, the former founder of what is now known as Cable & Wireless was mainly responsible for laying the first permanent trans-Atlantic cable in 1866. Since then, the company has laid cables world-wide, and ships are based in Singapore, Vigo (Spain), Suva (Fiji), and the North Pacific. The parent company was 'privatised' in 1986.

Name	Year	NRT	GRT	LOA	BM	DFT	SPD
Cable Enterprise	1964	1,386	4,358	113.6	14.9	5.8	13
Cable Guardian	1984	1,839	6,133	115.6	18	6.3	10
Cable Protector (1)	1976	699	1,599	81	17	4.7	10
Cable Venture (2)	1962	3,431	9,019	151.9	18.8	8.9	12
Mercury	1962	3,333	8,962	144.4	17.9	7.6	14.5
Retriever	1962	1,469	4,218	112.8	14.5	5.8	13
New building	1988	1,839	6,133	115.6	18	6.3	10

Notes: (1) Is a multi-role support vessel; all others are cable ships; (2) is used exclusively for cable-laying, others being employed in cable maintenance and repair.

6.1999 - Transfer to Global Marine Systems Ltd.
2000 - Still in service.

GB90. SEASPREAD   6081 grt   112.0 x 21.0 x 8.3
E Diesel-electric propulsion comprising 5 Nohab 16-cylinder oil engines driving 5 generators connected to 4 electric morors, single screw.
CT (4), **SS** (2).
1980 - Completed by Oresundsvarvet, Landskrona as *Stena Seaspread* for Stena A/B Group, Gothenburg as a diving maintenance ship.
1992 - Purchased by Cable & Wireless Ltd and converted for cablelaying/repairing for a maintenance contract based at Victoria(BC).
1996 - Converted into a permanent cablelayer/repairer based at Victoria(BC) for maintenance of Pacific cables.
6.1999 - Transfer to Global Marine Systems Ltd.
2000 - Still based at Victoria(BC).

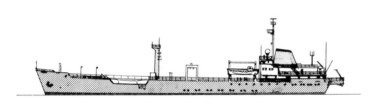

OCEAN SURVEYOR

GB91. OCEAN SURVEYOR   1949 grt   268.6 x 40.4 x 18.0
E Diesel engine, 1700 bhp. Single controllable pitch propeller.
Stern working survey ship.
7.1968 - Completed by Bijkers Aannemingsbedrijf, Gorinchen for J. Lauritzen as *Sirpa Dan*.
7.1968 - Converted to a cableship for the Great Northern Telegraph Company, renamed *Northern*. Bow thruster installed to help manoeurability. Employed mostly in Europe.
1988 - Sold to Cable & Wireless (Marine) Ltd name u/ch, arrived on the Bermuda station during 4.1989.
1990 - Converted into an oceanographical survey ship for a joint venture by Cable & Wireless (Marine) Ltd and Wimpole, renamed *Ocean Surveyor*. Employed surveying North and South Atlantic waters in 1991/92, Pacific & Australasian waters in 1993/94.
1995 - Sold to Louis Dreyfus Armateurs S.N.C., Panama name u/ch.
1999 - Still in service as a research ship.

GB92. SEAWAY FALCON   10385 grt   152.84 x 21.4 x 7.5
E Diesel-electric, twin screw. Five 16-cylinder oil engines driving 5 generators connected to four electric motors. 14 knots.
1976 - Completed by IHC Gusto N.V., Schiedam as drillship *Petrel*, sister of *Pelican* which was converted in 1993 into the cableship *C.S. Nexus* for BT Marine Ltd at Birkenhead.

1989 - Renamed *Oil Driller*

1990 - Renamed *Petrel*

1993 - Converted into a pipelayer/cablelayer. Unlike the *Pelican* conversion, she retains her central drilling tower and gained a high curved structure aft, around which steel pipes are led while laying and avoiding the use of a 'stinger'.

1995 - Renamed *Seaway Falcon* by SCS Shipping Ltd (Stolt Comex Seaway A/S).

GB93. CABLE INNOVATOR   14277 grt   145.5 x 24.0 x 8.5

E Diesel-electric propulsion comprising 5 Wartsila Vasa oil engines(three of 9-cylinder & two of 6-cylinder) connected to 5 electric generators. 15 knots. 4 thrusters.

CT (3) of total capacity 4874 cu. metres or 8,500 tonnes of cable with a fourth tank designed to carry spares with an inner ring separating up to 300 cu. metres of cable. Two cable lines, controlled by a 21 wheel pair linear cable engine & 4m diameter electrically-driven drum, starboard line of 16 tonnes capacity & port of 12 tonnes at 1.5 knots cable recovery speed.

SS (2) of 4 metres diameter over which an 'A' frame is fitted.

9.1995 - Completed by Kvaerner Masa Yards, Turku as twin-funnelled flagship of Cable & Wireless(Marine) Ltd, Chelmsford. $70M construction cost. 64 crew + 17 berths for cable technicians and observers.

1996 - Laying Asian Pacific Cable (APC) network between Taiwan/Hong Kong/Singapore/ Indonesia/Malaysia/Thailand & Philippines.

1996/97 - Laying optical fibre system between Australia/Indonesia.

1997/98 - FLAG global optical fibre system from Palermo,Sicily to Mara, Japan, other sections laid by six cableships from the Tyco, KDD and SBSS fleets.

1998 - Pan Americas optical fibre system in Caribbean, 2700 km system divided into seven segments from Chile/Peru/Ecuador/Panama/Colombia/Venezuela/Aruba to St. Croix and St. Thomas under contract from Tyco Submarine Systems Ltd (TSSL).

1998/99 - JIH (Japan Information Highway) encircling Japan, cablelaying with *C.S. Nexus*.

1999 - Southern Cross optical fibre system from Australia/New Zealand/Hawaii.

2000 - Japan/U.S.A. optical fibre cablelaying.

GB94. BOLD ENDEAVOUR   9388 grt   129.8 x 22.0 x 6.7

E Diesel-electric, 4 Wartsila 9-cylinder diesel alternators connected to 2 controllable pitch propellers, 13 knots. 2 stern azimuths, 3 forward thrusters.

CT (4) of 5,500 tonnes capacity or 8,820 km of cable, two of 16.5 m diameter of 2450 cu.m. total capacity for cable, and two spare tanks of 6.0m diameter for rope etc.

SS (2) of 3m diameter, one 21 wheel pair linear cable engine, one 4 wheel pair linear cable engine, 1 drum engine of 4m diameter.

30.7.1999 - Launched by Karen Winnick, wife of co-Chairman of Global Crossing and completed in 12.1999 by Van der Giessen de Noord, Holland for Global Marine Systems. Her £30M design incorporates the latest research into cableship design carried out by the Southampton Institute and the Netherlands Marim. She has a 6-deck forward bridge and accomodation block with accomodation for 90 crew + observers, and is designed for stern-working in up to Beaufort Force 6 winds and sea state 4 with 35 tonne stern 'A' frame. She has a clear cable deck of 300 sq.m. and partly sheltered deck of 1180 sq. m. with repeater stacks on the port side, and one crane of 5 tonnes and two cranes of 2 tonnes each. She has a wooden platform aft to stow the ROV and Seaplow, the latter operating up to depths of 1,000 metres.

WAVE VENTURE completing conversion on Tyneside in February, 2000 (Author).

WAVE SENTINEL completing conversion on Teesside in February, 2000 (Michael Green)

GB95. WAVE VENTURE   10076 grt   131.71 x 19.41 x 6.1

E 12-cylinder MaK oil engine sr geared to controllable pitch propeller. 4890 bhp. 14 knots, machinery aft. 2 thrusters.

CT (3), **SS** (2) with cable machinery configured for stern laying.

1982 - Completed by Fredrikshavn Vaerft A/S, Fredrikshavn as *Mercandian Governor* for Mercandia A/S (Per Henriksen), Copenhagen. Ro-ro 414 TEU.

1984 - Renamed *Governor*.

1985 - Renamed *Mercandian Governor*.

1988 - Transfer to Scandlines A/S, Copenhagen (K/S Merc-Skandia) and converted to a ro-ro passenger ship with accomodation for 500 deck passengers. Renamed *Kraka*.

7.1999 - Arrived at Hebburn-on-Tyne for conversion into a cablelayer for Global Marine Systems Ltd, Chelmsford, completed 1.2000 renamed *Wave Venture*.

GB96. WAVE MERCURY   10404 grt   131.71 x 19.41 x 6.1

E 12-cylinder MaK oil engine sr geared to controllable pitch propeller. 4890 bhp. 14 knots, machinery aft. 2 thrusters.

CT (3), **SS** (2) with cable machinery configured for stern laying.

1982 - Completed by Fredrikshavn Vaerft A/S, Fredrikshavn as *Mercandian President* for Mercandia A/S (Per Henriksen), Copenhagen. Ro-ro 414 TEU.

1984 - Renamed *President*.

1986 - Renamed *Mercandian President*.

1988 - Transfer to Scandlines A/S, Copenhagen (K/S Merc-Skandia) and converted to a ro-ro passenger ship with accomodation for 500 deck passengers. Renamed *Lodbrog*.

7.1999 - Arrived at Hebburn-on-Tyne for conversion into a cablelayer for Global Marine Systems Ltd, Chelmsford, completed 12.1999 renamed *Wave Mercury*.

GB97. WAVE SENTINEL   11166 grt   126.4 x 21.0 x 6.0

E Two 6-cylinder MaK oil engines dr geared to two controllable pitch propellers.   18 knots. 2 thrusters.

CT (3), **SS** (2) with cable machinery configured for stern-laying.

1995 - Completed by Koninklijke Scheldegroep B.V., Vlissingen for Commodore Shipping Ltd, Jersey (Condor Marine Services Ltd) as *Island Commodore*. Ro-ro 306 TEU.

9.1999 - Arrived Teesside for conversion into a cablelayer for Global Marine Systems, Chelmsford, completed 2.2000 and renamed *Wave Sentinel*.

GB98. WAVE ALERT   4416 grt   102.7 x 19.4 x 6.7

E 8-cylinder Wartsila oil engines connected to 2 controllable pitch propellers.

CT (2), **SS** (2) with cable machinery configured for stern-laying.

1983 - Completed by Marstrandverken, Marstrand as *Ugland Comex 1* for Ugland Comex Offshore.

1985 - Purchased by ITM Offshore Ltd, Middlesbrough renamed *ITM Installer*.

1986 - Purchased by Stena Offshore A/B renamed *Northern Installer*.

1992 - Purchased by Northern Contractors International Ltd (Cable & Wireless (Marine) Ltd & Ugland Offshore & Coflexip Stena Offshore), name unchanged.

1995 - Purchased by Flex Installer Offshore Ltd renamed *Flex Installer*.

1998 - Sold to Coflexip Stena Offshore Ltd renamed *CSO Installer*.

• We must receive your form/instructions no later than December 1s

SHIPPING
Today and Yesterday

I would like to take out a subscription to SHIPPING Today and Yesterday and starting with the following issue:

....

Subscription Rates:

	1 Year	2 Years
UK	£27.50 ☐	£50.00 ☐
Overseas Surface	£37.00 ☐	£66.00 ☐
Overseas Airmail	£58.00 ☐	£105.00 ☐

Payment Method:

Mastercard	☐	Visa/Delta	☐
American Express	☐	Switch	☐

Card No: ....

Switch Only { Expiry Date: ___/___
Start Date: ___/___
Issue No: _____

Name on card: ....

Signature: ....

OR

I enclose cheque/postal order (Sterling) made payable to **HPC Publishing.**

Return this (or a photocopy) to: HPC Publishing, Drury Lane, St Leonards-on-Sea, East Sussex TN38 9BJ, UK

Send The Magazines To:

Name: ....
Address: ....
....
Postcode: ....
Country: ....
Tel: ....

If this is a gift subscription, please answer the following questions:

Please send the first issue to me for Christmas
Please send renewals to me
My contact details are:

Name: ....
Address: ....
....
Postcode: ....
Country: ....
Tel: ....

Please tick if you do not wish to receive information regarding other products and services. ☐

Tic

The London-registered cable layer Wave Venture, 10,076grt, of Global Marine Systems, is a former ferry built by Frederikshavn Vaerft A/S, Frederikshavn, in 1982; she is the former Kraka, 2000; ex-Mercandian Governor,

WAVE ALERT completing conversion at Hebburn in May,2000.
Two complete decks have been built on to this former oil rig supply
vessel, with the upper deck being the cable deck. (Author)

1.2000 - Arrived Hebburn-on-Tyne for conversion into a cablelayer for Global Marine Systems Ltd, Chelmsford, completed 5.2000 renamed *Wave Alert.* Two additional decks have been built on to this former oil rig supply vessel, of which the upper deck is the cable deck leading to two large stern sheaves.

Close-up of the twin stern sheaves of
WAVE MERCURY   (Author)

GENERAL POST OFFICE.

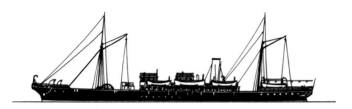

MONARCH(2)

GB99. MONARCH(2)   1122 grt   240.0 x 33.0 x 17.9
E Double expansion, single screw, 11 knots.
CT (3), **BS** (2).
1883 - Completed by David J. Dunlop & Co., Port Glasgow. First cable ship to be built for the G.P.O.
1891 - Laid first telephone cable across the Channel, manufactured by Siemens Bros.
8.1914 - Cut Borkum/Fayal German cable.
1914/15 - Maintaining and laying cables in Scapa Flow.
8.9.1915 - Mined/sunk 2.5 miles South of Folkestone, 3 crew killed.

GB100. ALERT(1)   See *Lady Carmichael* of Part I

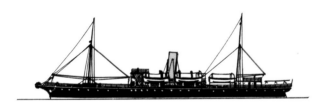

MONARCH(3)

GB101. MONARCH(3)   1150 grt   222.7 x 32.2 x 19.1
E Triple expansion engines, twin screw.
CT (3), **BS** (2) 65 crew.
1916 - Completed by Swan, Hunter & Wigham Richardson Ltd, Wallsend for G.P.O. primarily as a repair ship with two bow sheaves only. Employed in Home waters throughout her career.
1944 - Mistakenly shelled by American destroyers, all on deck killed, a junior deck officer brought her into port, repaired.
16.4.1945 - Torpedoed/sunk off Southwold.

GB102. ALERT(2)   941 grt   196.7 x 31.4 x 20.1
E Triple expansion, twin screw.
CT (3), **BS** (2).
1918 - Completed by Swan, Hunter & Wigham Richardson Ltd for G.P.O., a near sister of *Monarch*(3) but had bigger cable tanks and smaller bunker fuel capacity.
1942 - Laid experimental length of Hais petrol pipe in the Medway.
24.2.1945 - Torpedoed/sunk off the North Goodwins with loss of all hands.

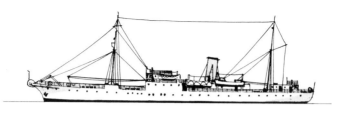

ARIEL

GB103. ARIEL   1479 grt   251.6 x 35.2 x 16.3
E Triple expansion, twin screw, 12 knots.
CT (3), **BS** (2).
1.9.1939 - Launched and 12.1939 - completed by Swan, Hunter & Wigham Richardson Ltd, Newcastle for G.P.O. Her sister *Iris*(2) and four war-built sisters for the Admiralty from the same yard were all very similar. A seventh member of this class was sold by the Admiralty to Trinity House after the end of the war, and launched at the Neptune yard of Swan's on 20th November,1945 as *Alert*, completing on 20th April,1946 with a grt of 1527 tons.
1940 - Laid Jersey/Pirou parragutta coaxial telephone cable.
1940 - Laid Dartmouth/Guernsey/Jersey parragutta coaxial telephone cable.
1954 - Laid Sicily/Malta coaxial telephone cable on charter to Cable & Wireless Ltd, who were the operators of the cable on behalf of NATO.
1954 - Lowestoft/Scheveningen 2 cables each with 4 repeaters.
1958 - Bournemouth/Guernsey/Jersey 10 repeaters.
4.1961 - Laid shore end at Oban of CANTAT1 Transatlantic telephone cable.
1962 - Colwyn Bay/Isle of Man 4 repeaters.
1969 - Renamed *C.S. Ariel*.
3.1973 - Laid shore end at Widemouth Bay(NS) for CANTAT2 Transatlantic cable.
1976 - Taken out of service and sold when *Monarch*(5) came into service. Broken up on the Medway during 12.1976.

GB104. IRIS(2)   1479 grt   251.6 x 35.2 x 16.3
E Triple expansion, twin screw, 12 knots.
CT (3), **BS** (2).
26.3.1940 - Launched and 6.1940 - completed by Swan, Hunter & Wigham Richardson Ltd, Newcastle for G.P.O.
1942 - Laid second experimental Hais petrol pipe in the Clyde.
24.6.1943 - Inserted the first ever submarine repeater into Anglesey/Port Erin(Isle of Man) coaxial cable laid the previous year. The repeater failed after five months but was replaced by a spare which lasted seven years.
1954 - Lowestoft/Scheveningen coaxial telephone cable 4 repeaters.
1956 - Sicily/Pantellaria/Tunisia coaxial telephone cable on charter to Cable & Wireless Ltd, who were the operators of the cable on behalf of NATO, 3 repeaters.
1958 - Anglo/Belgian coaxial from Dumpton Gap/Middlekerke 3 repeaters.
1969 - Renamed *C.S. Iris*.
1.6.1976 - Taken out of service and sold for scrap to Van der Marbel B.V., Middenweg, Nieuwekerk (Holland).

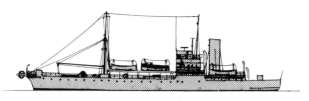

ALERT(3)

GB105. ALERT(3)   1460 grt   233.0 x 34.4 x 17.5
E Triple expansion, twin screw, 11 knots.
CT (3), **BS** (2).
1915 - Completed as *Nordeney* by Howaldtswerke, Kiel for the German Navy as an oil tanker.
1922 - Converted by Deutsche Werke, Rustringen into a cableship for Norddeutsche See-kabelwerke, cable tanks fitted at Bremerhaven.
1924 - Diverted the 1896 Borkum/Vigo cable into Dumpton Gap.
1925 - Malaga/Isla Alhucemas   (Spanish Govt.)
1926 - Warenemunde/Gedser(Denmark)   (Danish Govt.)
1926 - Aldeburgh/Domburg assisted by Neptun(1) (German Govt.)
1927/31 - Baltic cables linking Denmark, Sweden, Germany & Finland.
1931 - Ystad/Ronne(Bornholm)   (Swedish Govt.)
1931 - Barseback(Denmark)/Charlottenhund(Denmark) (Danish Govt.)
1938 - Heligoland/Wangeroge   (German Govt.)
1938 - Mariehamn/Norrtelje   (Swedish Govt.)
1940 - Sandefjord/Fredrikshavn(Denmark)   (Norwegian Govt.)
1945 - Handed over to G.P.O. as war reparations renamed *Alert*.
1946/60 - Post-war cablelaying/repairing to and on the Continent e.g. Germany/Denmark cable of 1956, stationed at Woolwich Dolphins with a London crew.
2.1960 - Taken out of service and broken up.

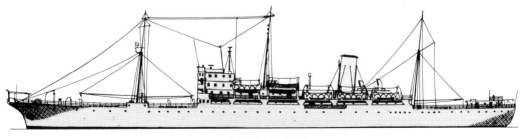

MONARCH(4)

GB106. MONARCH(4)   8056 grt   479.9 x 55.8 x 27.9
E Triple expansion, twin screw, 14.5 knots.
CT (4), **BS** (3).
10.1945 - Launched and 2.1946 - completed by Swan, Hunter & Wigham Richardson, Newcastle for G.P.O.
1947 - Aldeburgh/Domburgh coaxial telephone cable with *Alert*(3) (G.P.O.)
1950 - Weymouth/Fano   (Gt. Northern Telegraph Co.)
1952/54 - Cape Canaveral Atlantic tracking system (U.S.A.F.)

1953 - Recife/St. Vincent   (Italcable)
1954 - 4 power cables across the St. Lawrence   (Canadian Govt.)
1956 - TAT1 coaxial Oban/Clarenville(Nfl)/Nova Scotia (A.T. & T.)
1957 - San Francisco/Hawaii coaxial telephone   (A.T. & T.)
1959 - TAT2 coaxial France/Newfoundland/Nova Scotia   (A.T. & T.)
1961 - CANTAT1 coaxial Oban/Hampden(Nfl)   (C.& W./C.O.T.C.)
1962 - COMPAC Pacific coaxial Sydney/Auckland/Suva & Port Alberni/Hawaii with *Mercury*
1963 - Winterton/Borkum   (G.P.O./German Govt.)
1964 - SEACOM coaxial Singapore/Jesselton/Hong Kong & Guam/Madang/Cairns with *Mercury.*
1967 - Kristiansand/Thisted coaxial   (Norwegian Govt.)
1968 - Dorset/Jersey coaxial   (G.P.O.)
1968 - Scarborough/Kristiansand coaxial   (G.P.O.)
1969 - Renamed *C.S. Monarch*
13.10.1970 - Sold to Cable & Wireless Ltd renamed *Sentinel*(2) after a refit. Used as a repair ship based at Bermuda, and for Scarab submersible development.
25.10.1977 - Arrived Blyth for breaking up.

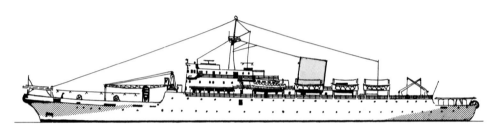

ALERT(4)

GB107. ALERT(4)   6413 grt   417.0 x 54.6 x 22.5
E Diesel-electric propulsion, twin screw. Bow thruster.
CT (3), **BS** (3), **SS** (1)
1961 - Completed by Fairfield Shipbuilding & Engineering Co. Ltd for G.P.O. Based at Southampton for repair and maintenance of Transatlantic telephone cables.
1961 - Manahawkin/Bermuda coaxial telephone cable   (A.T. & T.)
1961 - Corner Brook(NFL)/Nova Scotia segment of CANTAT1 (C.& W./C.O.T.C.)
1962 - CANTAT B Canadian links   (Canadian Govt.)
1962 - SCOTICE Scotland/Iceland/Greenland/Newfoundland (Gt. Northern Tel.Co.)
1963 - TAT3 Transatlantic coaxial telephone cable with *Long Lines*(A.T. & T.)
1967 - Nykoping/Ronne coaxial   (Danish Govt.)
1969 - Renamed *C.S. Alert.*
1969 - Goonhilly Down/Sesimbra coaxial   (G.P.O.)
1969 - Greece/Italy MED3 coaxial   (Greek Govt.)
1971 - Lerwick/Kirkwall; Winterton/Germany; Aldeburgh/Domburgh (G.P.O.)
1971 - Broadstairs/Ostend; Scarborough/Thisted(Denmark) (G.P.O.)
1972 - Dorset/Guernsey/Jersey   (G.P.O.)
1972 - West Palm Beach(Fa)/Provience(Bahamas)   (A.T. & T.)
1975 - Broadstairs/Domburgh(Neth)   (G.P.O.)
1975 - Palo(Italy)/Tel Aviv(Israel)   (Italian Govt.)

9.1986 - Laid first operational optical fibre cable U.K./Belgium, 3 repeaters 280 Mbits/sec.
27.10.1995 - Arrived Alang, India as *Al* for breaking up, having been sold via Rederi Gebroeder Wijsmuller B.V., Holland.

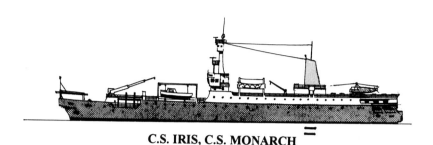

C.S. IRIS, C.S. MONARCH

GB108. C.S. MONARCH(5)   3936 grt   97.2 x 15.0 x 5.5
E 2 oil engines each of 2600 bhp, twin screw, 13.5 knots.
CT (4) and 6 auxiliary tanks alongside these in wings of ship. 'Pan' type vessel for rapid reloading of cable in port using portable cylindrical tanks lifted by shore cranes. 540 cu.m. or 1700 tonnes capacity. Based at Southampton at new cable depot opened in 1975.
BS (2), two 3m diameter drum engines, two haul off/hold back units, bow thruster, active rudder.
12.2.1975 - Launched and 1.1.1976 - completed by Robb - Caledon Shipbuilders Ltd, Dundee for G.P.O. as a repair ship based at Southampton for long-term maintenance contract with NSCMA (North Sea Cable Maintenance Agreement)
1983 - Transferred to BT(Marine) Ltd.
1994 - Cable & Wireless(Marine) Ltd became managers, owner Midland Montague Leasing.
12.1997 - Base transferred to Portland, and fitted with a heavy gantry on starboard side in front of the bridge to lift heavy submersibles.
6.1999 - Transfer to Global Marine Systems Ltd, Chelmsford. 62 officers & crew.
7.2000 - Still in commission.

GB109. C.S. IRIS(3)   3936 grt   309.9 x 49.2 x 15.5
E 2 oil engines each of 2600 bhp, twin screw, 13.5 knots.
CT (4) and 6 auxiliary tanks alongside these in wings of ship. 'Pan' type vessel for rapid reloading of cable in port using portable cylindrical tanks lifted by shore cranes. 540 cu.m. or 1700 tonnes capacity. Based at Southampton at new cable depot opened in 1975.
BS (2), two 3m diameter drum engines, two haul off/hold back units, bow thruster, active rudder.
2.10.1975 - Launched and 28.6.1976 completed by Robb - Caledon Shipbuilders Ltd, Dundee for G.P.O. as a repair ship based at Southampton for long-term maintenance contract with NSCMA (North Sea Cable Maintenance Agreement).
4.1982 - Operated as despatch vessel for seven months between Ascension and the Falklands.
1983 - Transferred to BT(Marine) Ltd.
1994 - Cable & Wireless(Marine) Ltd became managers, owner Midland Montague Leasing.
12.1997 - Base transferred to Portland
6.1999 - Transfer to Global Marine Systems Ltd, Chelmsford. 62 officers & crew.
7.2000 - Still in commission.

C.S. IRIS is seen at Southampton with her 'Pan' portable cable tanks being loaded (Top)

GB110. C.S. SOVEREIGN   11242 grt   127.3 x 21.0 x 7.0
E Diesel-electric propulsion comprising 3 Stork-Werkspoor oil engines/generators.
CT (4), total capacity 2800 cu. metres or 6200 tonnes. Cablelaying over the stern 4 m diameter sheave using the aft 40-tonne 4-metre diameter drum engine, cable pick-up/repair using bow sheave and two 40-tonne 3.5 metre diameter drum engines
1991 - Completed by Van de Giessen de Noord, Netherlands for BT Marine Ltd, Southampton.
1994 - Cable & Wireless (Marine) Ltd, Chelmsford became managers, owner BT Forty Ltd.
12.1997 - Base transferred to Portland for long-term maintenance contract with ACMA (Atlantic Cable Maintenance Agreement).
6.1999 - Transfer to Global Marine Systems Ltd.

**A fine view of the Dutch-built C.S. SOVEREIGN completed in 1991 for
BT Marine Ltd. She was one of five cableships amalgamated into the
cableship fleet of Cable & Wireless (Marine) Ltd in early 1995.**

GB111. C.S. NEXUS   11473 grt   150.5 x 25.0 x 7.8

E Diesel electric, five 16-cylinder oil engines/generators by Soc.Alsacienne de Constructeurs Mecaniques driving twin controllable pitch propellers. 12 knots. 5 thrusters.

CT (3) of total capacity 7,700 tonnes of cable, linear cable engine, stern sheaves.

1972 - Completed by IHC Gusto N.V., Schiedam as the drillship *Pelican* for Offshore Europe N.V. (Fina Marine S.A.,mgr) with tall drilling structure amidships and twin funnels aft.

1985 - Renamed *Pelican II.*

1993 - Purchased by Coe Metcalf Shipping Ltd, Liverpool (James Fisher & Sons, mgr) and time-chartered to BT Marine. Converted by Cammell, Laird & Co. Ltd, Birkenhead into a cableship, removing the drill structure, fitting a new bridge forward and installing cable tanks and machinery. Plough launched by 'A' frame over the stern. Accomodation for 23 crew and 55 cable technicians and observers. Renamed *C.S. Nexus.*

1994 - Time charter transferred to Cable & Wireless(Marine) Ltd.

1998 - Laying JIH (Japan Information Highway).

6.1999 - Transfer to Global Marine Systems Ltd on long-term charter to Alcatel Submarine Networks working on Japan/U.S.A. systems.

ROYAL NAVY.

KILMUN

GB112. KILMUN   640 grt
E Triple expansion, single screw.
CT (2), **BS** (1).
1915 - Built as a *'Kil'* class gunboat and used for a time as a 'Q' ship.
1917 - Converted for harbour defence cablelaying.
1922 - Fitted with Johnson & Phillips single paying-out/picking-up machine on fore deck.
1947 - Sold to Norwegian company for coastal trading.
1948 - Foundered.

LASSO

GB113. LASSO   1152 grt   202.5 x 35.2 x 11.75
E Triple expansion, twin screw.
CT (2), **BS** (1), no facilities for stern laying. Johnson & Phillips cable machinery.
1938 - Completed by John I. Thornycroft Ltd, Southampton.
5.1947 - Joined the Admiralty Cable Service, Royal Fleet Auxiliary.
1959 - Sold for breaking up.

GB114. HOLDFAST   2988 grt   250.5 x 35.3 x 21.1
E Triple expansion, single screw.
CT (2), **BS** (2), **SS** (1).
1921 - Completed by Hawthorns & Co. Ltd, Leith as *London* for Dundee, Perth & London Shipping Co. Ltd for East coast passenger trade. 1491 grt.
29.8.1937 - Collision/sunk off Humber L.V., raised & returned to service.
28.8.1939 - Requisitioned by Admiralty as an examination vessel, renamed *Holdfast* 10.1939.
8.1940 - Returned to owners.
1.1942 - Requisitioned by Admiralty for conversion to a pipelaying vessel for the 'Pluto' project of transporting petrol under the Channel at D-Day.
7.1942 - Three month conversion on Thames by R.& H. Green & Silley Weir Ltd.
12.1942 - Laid first experimental length of 2" Hais petrol pipe across the Bristol Channel from Swansea to Ilfracombe.

8.1944 - 10.1944 - Laid two 3" petrol pipes between Sandown(I. of W.)/Cherbourg; as well as eleven from Dungeness/Boulogne (9 of 3" & 2 of 2"); in addition to six steel 'Hamel' pipes laid between Dungeness/Boulogne. She was assisted by three other merchant ships converted during 1943/44: *Algerian, Empire Ridley* and *Empire Baffin*, and five Thames motor barges for laying of shore ends.

7.1946 - Sold to Ministry of Transport and renamed *Empire Taw* for recovery of 'Pluto' pipelines.

9.1952 - Sold for use as a hulk and towed to Passage West, Cork.

1953 - Broken up there.

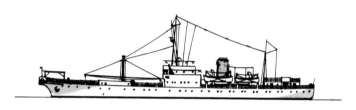

**BULLFINCH, BULLFROG, BULLHEAD,
ST. MARGARETS**

GB115. BULLFINCH   1512 grt   245.8 x 36.5 x 16.4

E Triple expansion, twin screw, 12 knots.

CT (3), **BS** (3).

1940 - Completed by Swan, Hunter & Wigham Richardson Ltd for harbour defence work.

1944 - First ship into Chios after the German evacuation, and then laid a cable at Piraeus.

1946 - Based at Malta with Mediterranean fleet, also doing charter work from there for Cable & Wireless Ltd and Italcable.

3.1947 - Transfer to Royal Fleet Auxiliary based at Turnchapel, Plymouth.

6.1953 - Present at Spithead Coronation Review.

1961 - Refit and fitted with 'A' frame gantry for handling rigid repeaters.

8.8.1975 - Taken out of service, laid-up at Plymouth.

14.2.1980 - Arrived Blyth for scrapping.

GB116. BULLFROG   1538 grt   252.0 x 36.4 x 22.3

E Triple expansion, twin screw, 12 knots.

CT (3), **BS** (3).

1944 - Completed by Swan, Hunter & Wigham Richardson Ltd for harbour defence work.

1946 - Sold to Cable & Wireless Ltd renamed *Retriever*(4).

1951/59 - Based at Singapore.

1961 - Sold to Commercial Cable Company renamed *Cable Restorer*.

7.1972 - Sold to South Atlantic Cable Corporation & based at Cape Town as guardship for S. Africa/U.K. SAT1 coaxial telephone cables, laid by *Mercury* and *John W. Mackay* in 1969 via Ascension Island.

1993 - Gifted to Simonstown Maritime Museum.

1999 - Still at Simonstown.

GB117. ST. MARGARETS 1524 grt   260.0 x 36.5 x 16.4
E   Triple expansion, twin screw, 12 knots.
CT (3), **BS** (3)
13.10.1943 - Launched and 1.1944 - completed by Swan, Hunter & Wigham Richardson Ltd for harbour defence work. Originally fitted with one 4" and four 20mm guns but this armament was later removed.
6.1944 - In support of Normandy landings.
1944/45 - Australian cablelaying and return voyage via Suez Canal recovering Port Said and Alexandria harbour defence cables and transporting them back to the U.K.
7.1947/3.1948 - Refit at Sheerness and transfer to Royal Fleet Auxiliary based at Turnchapel, Plymouth.
1948 - Charter to Cable & Wireless Ltd for renewal of Marseilles/Barcelona telegraph cable. Whilst securing a shore end at Marseilles in 6.1948 she towed the French liner *Ville d'Ajaccio* off the detached breakwater of stone blocks using one of her own cables.
1949/51 - In the Mediterranean on commercial charter and Admiralty work based at Malta. Repaired the Palermo/Cagliari telegraph cable.
1951/58 - Employed on a number of stations including Home waters, Mediterranean and Red Sea.
1958 - Laid-up at Plymouth but back in service a year later.
1961 - Converted into a dual purpose cablelayer/underwater research ship with no. 3 cable tank converted into a sophisticated electronics laboratory. Accomodation was updated with central heating for her 64 crew and visiting scientists. She divided her time during the next twenty years into equal amounts of cablelaying and research/experimental work.
1975 - Transfer to Royal Maritime Auxiliary Service.
1980 - Refitted for 22 weeks at Devonport.
6.1981 - Cablelaying in North European waters but her field of operations extended to Gibraltar, Madeira, Azores and the North Atlantic.
1985 - Laid-up and 7.2.1986 arrived Portsmouth in tow from Devonport having been sold to Pounds of Portsmouth. Subsequently broken up.

GB118. BULLHEAD   1538 grt   252.0 x 36.4 x 22.3
E   Triple expansion, twin screw, 12 knots.
CT (3), **BS** (3).
1945 - Completed by Swan, Hunter & Wigham Richardson Ltd for harbour defence work.
1946 - Sold to Cable & Wireless Ltd renamed *Electra*(2).
5.1948 - 1958 - Based in the West Indies.
1959 - Sold to Commercial Cable Company renamed *Cable Guardian*.
21.6.1964 - Arrived Inverkeithing for breaking up.

NEWTON

GB119. NEWTON   2779 grt   323.0 x 52.5 x 15.4
E   Diesel-electric propulsion 2700 bhp, single screw, 15 knots, 52 crew.
CT (2), **BS** (3).
25.6.1975 - Launched and 6.1976 completed by Scott's Shipbuilding Co. Ltd, Greenock as a dual-purpose cablelayer/sonar propagation trials ship/oceanographic research ship. Her bow rudder and thruster give maximum manoeuvrability at low speed.   The Royal Maritime Auxiliary Service have used her sophisticated electronics laboratory for various research and trials work in Arctic and Atlantic waters.
1980/81 - Out of service due to problems with diesel-electric machinery.
7.1994 - Damaged by onboard explosion off Florida coast.
2000 - Still in service with Defence Research Agency.

NEWTON carries out many subsea roles including cablelaying.

UNITED STATES of AMERICA
I. CABLESHIPS OWNED BY CABLE OWNERS

US1. PROFESSOR MORSE   See *Suffolk* of 1866 GB10

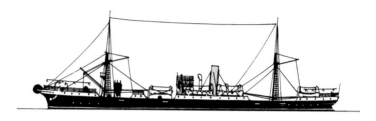

MACKAY-BENNETT

US2. MACKAY-BENNETT   1700 grt   270.0 x 40.0 x 24.5
E   Compound, twin screw, coal-fired.
CT (3), **BS** (1).
1884 - Completed by John Elder & Co., Govan for the Commercial Cable Company. Design features such as bow rudder and swivelling bow sheave came from *Faraday*(1), and she repaired the Transatlantic cables laid by *Faraday*(1) for the company, whose two principal directors were John W. Mackay, an American mining magnate, and Gordon Bennett, proprietor of the New York Herald. Stationed at Halifax(NS).
1905 - Laid Canadian shore end of a fourth Transatlantic cable for the company, assisting *Colonia, Anglia* and *Cambria* of Telcon.
1906 - Diverted a Transatlantic cable ending at Canso(NS) into St. John's(NFL).
15.4.1912 - Chartered by White Star Line to search for bodies from *Titanic*. She carried a chaplain and several morticians and her partly ice-filled cable tanks were used as a mortuary.
1922 - Reduced to cable storage hulk in Plymouth Sound.
22.9.1965 - Left Plymouth in tow for Ghent for scrapping.

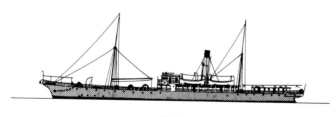

RELAY

US3. RELAY   1198 grt   240.0 x 32.2 x 14.2
E   Triple expansion, twin screw.
CT (3), **BS** (1).
1890 - Completed by R. Thompson & Son, Sunderland for Central & South American Telegraph Company.
1890 - Connected Guatemala into West Coast Central American cables.

2.1920 - Transfer to All America Cables on formation, based at Montevideo for maintenance of E. Coast of South America cables.

1932 - Sold to Dutch East Indies Exploring Company, Nevada name unchanged.

1937 - Sold to Chinese owners renamed *Elli*.

1940 - Wrecked but salvaged and renamed *Bjornefjell* of Norway in 1942.

1947 - Sold to Finnish owners renamed *Bota*.

1948 - Sold to Rederi A/B Finn, Helsingfors, Finland renamed *Finn*.

1952 - Broken up in Norway.

US4. MEXICAN   See *Duchess of Marlborough* GB28
US5. SCOTIA   See Great Britain GB27
US6. RESTORER   See Great Britain GB50

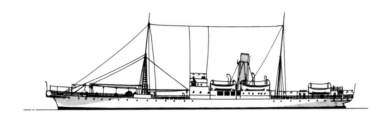

GUARDIAN

US7. GUARDIAN   1768 grt   278.4 x 36.0 x 14.1
E Triple expansion, twin screw, 12.5 knots.
CT (4), **BS** (3).
1907 - Completed by Swan, Hunter & Wigham Richardson Ltd for Central & South American Telegraph Company.
2.1920 - Transfer to All America Cables on formation, based West coast for maintenance of Pacific cables.
1940 - Sold to United Fruit Co. name unchanged.
1946 - Sold to Caribbean Atlantic Shipping Corporation renamed *Ceibar*.
1948 - Sold to Ships & Vessels Ltd, Israel renamed *Theodore Herzel*.
1951 - Broken up.

US8. FLAURENCE WARD   207 grt   105.9 x 24.4 x 14.3
E Compound fitted in 1908.
1907 - Completed by Bendixsen Shipbuilding Co., Eureka(California) as a wooden sailing ship for the Commercial Pacific Cable Company for small repair jobs on Pacific cables.
1924 - Sold to Inter-Island S.N. Company of Hawaii renamed *Molokai*.
1936 - Sold to Cia Maritima de Navigation, Guaymas, Mexico name unchanged.
1943 - Broken up.

US9. ROBERT C. CLOWRY   532 grt   132.3 x 33.3 x 15.1
E Compound, twin screw.
CT (1), **BS** (1).
1910 - Completed by A. C. Brown & Sons, New York for Western Union Telegraph Company for shallow water repair work off North American coasts.
1924 - Sold.

GEORGE WARD

US10. GEORGE WARD   1608 grt   251.0 x 34.8 x 18.7

E   Triple expansion, single screw.

CT (2), **BS** (3).

1898 - Completed by Laird Bros., Birkenhead as *Princess Alice* for the Prince of Monaco for oceanographical research.

1902 - Purchased by Lord Inverclyde as his private steam yacht *Beryl*.

1921 - Purchased by Commercial Cable Company and converted by Barclay, Curle & Co. Ltd into a cableship at Govan renamed *George Ward*. Based at Plymouth as company's European repair ship.

1923 - Broken up.

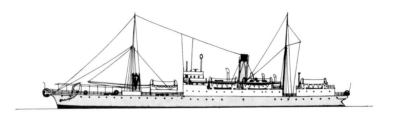

ALL AMERICA

US11. ALL AMERICA   1819 grt   278.4 x 37.0 x 22.4

E   Triple expansion, twin screw.

CT (4) (3 forward and 1 aft), **BS** (3), **SS** (1). 1750 tons cable capacity.

1921 - Completed by Swan, Hunter & Wigham Richardson Ltd for All America Cables as a duplicate of *Guardian*. She was used for the maintenance of Caribbean, West Coast Central America, and South American cables. Her first Master was Capt. Taylor of *Guardian*.

1939 - Chartered by Cable & Wireless Ltd for Brazilian station.

1946/47 - Chartered by Cable & Wireless Ltd for West Indies station.

13.9.1961 - Arrived Charleston, North Carolina for breaking up.

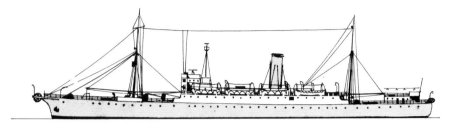

JOHN W. MACKAY

US12. JOHN W. MACKAY   4064 grt   361.8 x 48.1 x 25.4
E Two triple expansion engines, twin screw, 14 knots. 10,000 mile steaming range.
CT (4), **BS** (3), **SS** (1). Telcon cable machinery, Lucas dynamometers.
30.11.1922 - Launched by Swan, Hunter & Wigham Richardson Ltd for Commercial Cable
Company. Some design features shared with *Faraday*(2) which were both launched on the
Tyne within a few days of each other. Replaced *Mackay-Bennett* at Halifax(NS).
1924 - Waterville(Eire)/Weston-super-Mare   (Commercial Cable Company)
1929 - After serious interuption of communication due to subterranean upheaval between
Azores and Newfoundland, several telegraph cables had to be restored. She was one of seven
cableships involved in this, the others being *Faraday, Dominia, Cyrus Field, Lord Kelvin, All
America* and *Edouard Jeramec*.
1939/42 - Stationed at Halifax(NS) maintaining North Atlantic telegraph cables.
1942 - Requisitioned by Admiralty to lay cables in the Persian Gulf, Eastern Mediterranean.
Due to an acute shortage of cable, one of her first duties was to recover some 450 miles of
Italian cable lying off Cape Verde Isles from a depth of 2,000 fathoms.
1944 - Cablelaying in the Pacific for U.S. Navy.
1950 - Newfoundland/Greenland 'hot' line strategic cable   (U.S. Govt.)
1959 - Chartered to assist with TAT2 Transatlantic coaxial laying with *Monarch*(4).
1962 - SCOTICE Scotland/Iceland/Greenland/Newfoundland along with *Alert*(4).
1.1965 - Thoroughly modernised, her large deck areas made her suitable for conversion for
coaxial telephone cablelaying on charter to Standard Telephones & Cables, Greenwich.
1965 - Spain/Canaries coaxial   (Spanish Govt.)
1966/67 - Cape Kennedy Tracking System cables to Grand Turk & Bahamas (U.S.A.F.)
1969 - SAT1 coaxial Sesimbra(Port.)/Tenerife/Cape Verde Is/Ascension Is/South Africa.
1969 - Sicily/Libya & Civitavecchia/Golfo d'Aranci   (Italian Govt.)
1969 - Burg(Germany)/Malmo 121 n.m. & 15 repeaters   (German Govt.)
1970 - Estepona/Palo(Italy) 990 n.m. & 93 repeaters   (A.T. & T.)
1971 - Grand Canaria/Fuerteventura/Lanzarote   (Spanish Govt.)
1971 - Barcelona/Majorca   (Spanish Govt.)
1971·- Lerwick/Thorshavn(Faeroes) 230 n.m. 27 repeaters (U.K.G.P.O.)
1972 - PENBAL extension between Grand Canaria/Tenerife(Spanish Govt.)
1972 - Sesimbra(Port.)/Madeira 582 n.m 34 repeaters   (Portuguese Govt.)
1973 - St. Thomas/St. Maarten/Curacao   (All America Cables)
1975 - Cairns/Port Moresby coaxial   (Australian Govt.)
1977 - Laid-up at buoys off Greenwich, just downstream from the National Maritime
Museum. She had completed a record 55 years of cablelaying/repairing.
1990 - Transferred to dry-dock at Hebburn-on-Tyne for possible preservation.
3.1994 - Sold to Turkisk breakers and towed from the Tyne to Portsmouth and on to Aliaga,
arriving 25.3.1994 for scrapping.

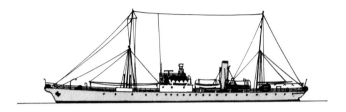

MARIE LOUISE MACKAY

US13. MARIE LOUISE MACKAY   1378 grt   234.0 x 34.2 x 22.2
E Triple expansion, twin screw, 12 knots.
CT (3), **BS** (3), **SS** (1).
1922 - Completed by Swan, Hunter & Wigham Richardson Ltd for Commercial Cable Company as a smaller repair ship.
4.8.1961 - Arrived Bruges for scrapping.

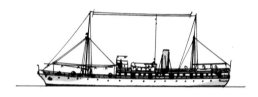

DICKENSON

US14. DICKENSON   831 grt   174.3 x 30.1 x 21.8
E Triple expansion, single screw.
CT (1), **BS** (2)
1923 - Completed by Sun Shipbuilding & Dry Dock Co, Chester(Pa) for the Commercial Pacific Cable Company. Accomodation for 12 passengers for her supplementary duties of supply ship to cable stations on remote Pacific islands. Based at Honolulu.
1.1946 - Foundered and sank.

CYRUS FIELD

US15. CYRUS FIELD   1288 grt   223.6 x 34.2 x 16.6
E Triple expansion, twin screw.
CT (3), **BS** (3)
1924 - Completed by Chantiers et Ateliers de St. Nazaire for Western Union Telegraph Company. A similar but smaller design of *Lord Kelvin* based at Halifax(NS).
7.1966 - Sold for scrapping at the same time as *Lord Kelvin*, and arrived at La Spezia in tow on 27.12.1966.

7.1966 - Sold for scrapping at the same time as *Lord Kelvin*, and arrived at La Spezia in tow on 27.12.1966.

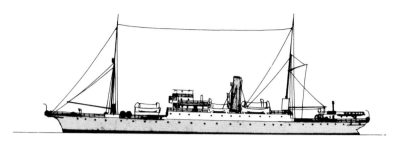

EDOUARD JERAMEC

US16. EDOUARD JERAMEC   2316 grt   289.2 x 41.1 x 23.7
E   Triple expansion, twin screw.
CT (3), **BS** (3), **SS** (1).
1913 - Completed by Forges et Chantiers de Grayville for Cie Francaise des Cables Telegraphiques as a repair ship for North Atlantic cables based at Le Havre.
1929 - Sold to All America Cables and after a refit was engaged on the maintenance of the New York/Colon cables. Name unchanged.
1946 - Sold to French Govt. P.T.T., renamed *Pierre Picard* for repair of the French Atlantic cables including those of the vessel's first owners, whose cables were taken over by the P.T.T. in 1945.
1948 - Refitted & converted to oil-burning, and undertook the reconditioning of the Brest/Cape Cod cable.
19.12.1952 - Sank in Brest harbour.

US17. CABLE GUARDIAN   See *Electra* in British section

US18. CABLE RESTORER   See *Bullfrog* in British section

US19. NEPTUN   See German Section

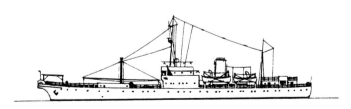

CABLE GUARDIAN, CABLE RESTORER

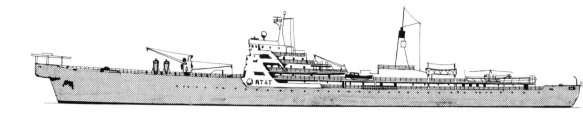

LONG LINES

US20. LONG LINES   11326 grt   511.6 x 69.9 x 26.9

E   Turbo-electric propulsion of 8500 s.h.p., twin screw, 15 knots.

CT (3), 3 spare tanks also provided for repair cable; linear cable engine at the stern and two forward electrically-driven cable machines.

BS (3) of ten feet diameter.

24.9.1961 - Launched by Schlieker Werft, Hamburg and 4.1963 completed by Deutsche Werft, Hamburg for Transoceanic Cableship Co Inc, a subsidiary of A. T. & T.

Largest cablelayer since *Dominia* of 1926.

5.1963 - Loaded at Southampton from the S.T.C. factory some 3518 n.m. of coaxial cable and 182 repeaters for the TAT3 Transatlantic cable from Widemouth Bay(Cornwall) to Tuckerton(NJ), assisted by *Alert*(4).

6.1964 - U.S.A./Japan coaxial telephone cable via Hawaii/Midway/Wake/Guam. The Oahu/Sagami Bay segment was of 5282 n.m. and 276 repeaters, and a connection was made at Hawaii to the British Commonwealth COMPAC system.

11.1964 - Philippines/Guam 1468 n.m. & 76 repeaters.

12.1964 - Vero Beach(Fa)/St. Thomas 1179 n.m. & 61 repeaters.

7.1965 - Tuckerton(NJ)/St. Hiliaire(France) TAT4 coaxial of 3600 n.m. length & 186 repeaters. *Marcel Bayard* laid the French shore end.

1968 - Jacksonville(Fa)/St. Thomas 1298 n.m. & 140 repeaters.

1968 - St. Thomas/Santo Domingo(Dominican Rep.) 386 n.m. & 20 repeaters.

1970 - Rhode Island/Conil(Spain) TAT5 coaxial of 3461 n.m. & 361 repeaters with extension from Estepona(Spain) to Palo(Italy).

1974/75 - San Luis(California)/Hawaii/Guam/Okinawa 7607 n.m. & 765 repeaters.

1976 - Rhode Island/St. Hiliaire(France) TAT6 coaxial 3600 n.m. & 745 repeaters. *Vercors* laid both shore ends.

1977/78 - Vancouver/Hawaii & California/Hawaii with connections to new Hawaii/Japan cable.

1979/80 - Florida/Guatemala & St. Thomas/Maiqueta.

1980/90 - Further laying/repairing in Pacific based at Honolulu - laid TPC4 optical fibre cable between North America/Japan in 1990.

1990/99 - Based at Honolulu for laying/repairing of California/Hawaii/Guam/Japan cables.

2000 - Still in service.   Blu 2003 June

US21. PEGGY G.   293 grt   181.6 x 35.0 x 8.3

E   Two diesel engines, twin screw.

1966 - Completed by Halter Marine, Pascagoula as an oil rig supply vessel modified to include two bow sheaves, removable deck reel stowage and a paying-out machine. Also used for oceanography and diving work and she has a helicopter platform fitted aft.

1982 - Sold & renamed *Blue Water II*.

1990 - Sold and renamed *Sidney Solar*.

1994 - Sold & renamed *Linda L*.

US22. A.B. WOOD II   195 grt   150.0 x 36.0 x 9.0
E Two diesel engines, twin screw.
BS (3)
1965 - Completed by Bishop SB Corp., Arabsas Pass, Texas as oil rig supply vessel *Leo Jude* later renamed *Lord Reyleigh*.
1972 - Purchased by Tracor Marine and converted into an acoustical survey ship/cableship. Cable reels stored on deck aft. Hydrophones lifted into the sea by crane. Bow thruster and active rudder fitted for precise positioning. Renamed *A. B. Wood II*.
1999 - Operating as a survey and research ship for Cavanagh Leasing Corp., Miami.

US23. CHARLES L. BROWN   2834 grt   339.7 x 41.5 x 18.6
E Two 7-cylinder Fiat diesel engines and diesel-electric for secondary propulsion, twin screw.
CT (3), **BS** (3), **SS** (1).
1953 - Launched and 1956 completed by Navalmeccanica Castellamare di Stabia, Naples for Cia Italiana Navi Cablografiche as *Salernum*. Chartered to Italian Govt. P.T.T. and Italcable as required. Hydrographic & oceanographic research/cableship.
1956/75 - Repair/laying of Mediterranean telegraph and telephone cables, with occasional repair of North Atlantic and Baltic cables. Surveys conducted throughout the length of the Mediterranean.
1984 - Sold to Transoceanic Cableship Co Inc, Morristown(NJ), a subsidiary of A.T. & T.
1986 - Renamed *Charles L. Brown*, and used for A.T. & T. cable repairs.
2000 - Still in service.

US24. GLOBAL SENTINEL   13201 grt   144.78 x 21.6 x 11.3
E Diesel electric propulsion comprising three Wartsila 12-cylinder oil engines driving three generators connected to electric motors. 4 thrusters, 2 forward and 2 aft.
12.10.1990 - Launched and 1991 completed by Far East - Levingston Shipbuilders Ltd, Singapore for C.S. Global Sentinel Partnership (Transoceanic Cable Ship Co. Inc).
1991 - Laid TPC-4 Pacific optical fibre system and TAT10 Transatlantic optical fibre system.
1997 - Transferred to Tyco Submarine Systems Ltd (TSSL). Based at Baltimore for North Atlantic cable repair work.

US25. GLOBAL LINK   13201 grt   144.78 x 21.6 x 11.3
E Diesel-electric propulsion comprising three Wartsila 12-cylinder oil engines driving three generators connected to electric motors. 4 thrusters, 2 forward and 2 aft.
1991 - Completed by Far East - Levingston Shipbuilders Ltd, Singapore for C.S. Global Link Partnership (Transoceanic Cable Ship Co. Inc).
1997 - Transferred to Tyco Submarine Systems Ltd (TSSL). Based at Baltimore for North Atlantic cable repair work.

US26. GLOBAL MARINER   12518 grt   145.66 x 21.6 x 11.3
E Diesel-electric propulsion comprising three Wartsila 12-cylinder oil engines driving three generators connected to 2 electric motors. 4 thrusters, 2 forward and 2 aft.
1992 - Completed by Far East - Levingston Shipbuilders Ltd, Singapore for C.S. Global Mariner Partnership (Transoceanic Cable Ship Co. Inc). Part-owner is Canada Teleglobe.
1997 - Transferred to Tyco Submarine Systems Ltd (TSSL). Based at Baltimore for North Atlantic cable repair work.

US27. COASTAL CONNECTOR   3969 grt   88.0 x 18.3 x 4.3
E   Two Polar 12-cylinder oil engines by A/B Bofors Nohab, 3 thrusters, 13 knots.
CT (2), **SS** (2)
1979 - Completed by G. Eides Sonner A/S Hoylandsbygdi as oil rig supply ship *Sulair*.
1989 - Sold and renamed *TNT Puma*.
1990 - Sold and renamed *Toisa Puma*.
1995 - Sold to Transoceanic Cableship Co. Inc (Dockwise N.V.,mgr) and converted into a cablelayer with two stern sheaves, renamed *Coastal Connector*.
2000 - Still in service with Tyco Submarine Systems Ltd (TSSL).

US28. TYCO PROVIDER   9226 grt   139.4 x 20.25 x 6.2
E   Two 6-cylinder Pielstick oil engines geared to two screw shafts, four thrusters, 14 knots.
CT (5) installed in Romania, ballast tanks rearranged.
1978 - Completed by Hollming O/Y, Rauma as heavy-lift/barge carrier *Stakhanovets Yermolenko* for Russian Navy.
1998 - Purchased by Coastal Cableship Co. and converted by the Daewoo Mangalia Dockyard in Romania into a stern cablelayer, and fitted with Dutch-manufactured cable handling machinery at Rotterdam by Niehuis & Van den Berg. 1100 tonnes of new steel inserted to make a 'tween deck and a cable deck, and existing coamings raised to give an enclosed space. Four Caterpillar generators were installed in a new generator room, and four Schottel azimuth thrusters were fitted. New ventilation and fire-fighting systems fitted. Renamed *Tyco Provider* for long-term charter to Tyco Submarine Systems Ltd (TSSL).

US29. OCEANIC PRINCESS   8966 grt   120.2 x 21.0 x 6.7
E   16-cylinder Wartsila oil engine.
1984 - Completed by Rauma-Repola O/Y, Rauma as ro-ro *Solano* for Henry Nielsen, Finland.
1994 - Sold to Finnlines O/Y, Helsinki renamed *Finnpine*.
6.2000 - Arrived at Viktor Lenac shipyard, Rijeka (Croatia) for conversion into a cablelayer for Caldwell Cable Ventures, a subsidiary of General Dynamics. Cable tanks and cable machinery to be installed and conversion completed by 10.2000. Renamed *Oceanic Princess*.

US30. OCEANIC PEARL   4629 grt   92.0 x 18.0 x 5.1
E   S.K.L. oil engine geared to single screw shaft.
1997 - Completed by Gemyat A/S, Tuzla as ro-ro *Kulachan*.
1997 - Sold to Pearl Lines Co. Ltd, Valletta renamed *Mother of Pearl*.
6.2000 - Arrived at Viktor Lenac shipyard, Rijeka (Croatia) for conversion into a cablelayer for Caldwell Cable Ventures, a subsidiary of General Dynamics. Cable tanks and cable machinery to be installed and conversion completed by 10.2000. Renamed *Oceanic Pearl*.

Late Addition
Tyco Submarine Systems Ltd have two cablelayers of 7800 dwt on order at Keppel Hitachi Zosen, Singapore for delivery in late 2000 and 2001 at a cost of $75M. This increases the size of the Tyco fleet into double figures.

II. U.S. MILITARY CABLESHIPS

US31. HOOKER   2085 grt   333.0 x 33.0 x 24.1
E Compound, single screw.
CT (3), **BS** (1).
11.1875 - Completed as *Branksome Hall* by London & Glasgow Shipbuilding Co., Glasgow for Hall Line, Liverpool..
1890 - Sold to Cia Transatlantica, Barcelona renamed *Panama*.
1898 - Captured in the West Indies by U.S. cruiser *Mangrove* during Spanish/U.S. war.
1900 - After service as troop transport, converted into a cableship for U.S. Army by Morse yard, Brooklyn, renamed *Hooker*.
1900 - Sailed from New York via Gibraltar and Suez Canal to Philippines to lay 240 n.m. of cable. During cablelaying she grounded on Corregidor island in Manila Bay and became a total loss.

US32. ROMULUS   809 grt   210.0 x 29.2 x 15.3
E Compound, single screw.
CT (1), **BS** (1)
6.1879 - Completed by H. MacIntyre, Paisley for McLeod & Co.,Manila
1900 - Converted into a cableship for U.S. Army for cablelaying in the Philippines.
1901 - Returned to owners, Cia Maritima of Manila.

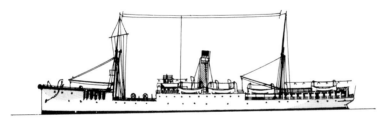

BURNSIDE

US33. BURNSIDE   2226 grt   285.2 x 36.7 x 26.0
E Compound, single screw, 10 knots.
CT (2), **BS** (2).
3.1882 - Completed by Campbell, Mackintosh & Bowstead of Newcastle as *Yeoman* for Australian trade of W. Lund, London.
1887 - Reboilered & re-engined by C.S. Swan & Hunter, Wallsend.
1891 - Sold to Spanish owners renamed *Rita*.
1898 - Captured by U.S. cruiser *Yale*, used by the U.S. Army as *Burnside*.
1900 - After the loss of *Hooker* she was converted into a cableship to complete the Philippine cables.
1904 - Laid first Seattle/Alaska telegraph cable.
1924 - Broken up.

US34. SAMUEL MILLS(1)   750 grt   166.5 x 32.5 x 11.5
E Triple expansion, single screw, 12 knots.
1909 - Completed for U.S. Army for coastal cablelaying.
1922 - Transferred to U.S. Coastguard, later renamed *Pequot*.

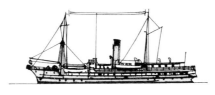

JOSEPH HENRY

US35. JOSEPH HENRY   842 grt   142.0 x 32.0 x 11.8
E Compound by builder, twin screw.
CT (1), **BS** (2), cable drum located on fo'c'stle, which was connected by cat walk to wooden bridge on starboard side only, cable machinery, buoys & grapnels in well deck. Two decks of accomodation, upper of teak.
1909 - Completed by Newport News Shipbuilding & Drydock Company for U.S. Signal Corps used on harbour defence cables on Eastern seaboard and Gulf of Mexico waters.
1939 - The only U.S. Govt.-owned cableship in commission.
1947 - Sold to Greek Govt. for telegraph maintenance duties renamed *Thalis O. Milissios*
1968 - Over one hundred cables in Greek waters maintained by Greek Govt., only three owned by Cable & Wireless Ltd.
1991 - Taken out of service and converted into a floating museum ship at the Greek Maritime Museum, Glyfada marina. Her cable tank now contains photographs of ships and men from the Greek Merchant Navy.

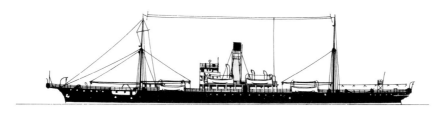

DELLWOOD

US36. DELLWOOD   3478 grt   320.7 x 46.0 x 24.5
E Triple expansion, single screw, 10 knots.
CT (3), **BS** (2), fo'c'stle connected to bridge by decking on port side only.
1919 - Completed by Hanlon Shipbuilding & Drydock Company, Oakland.
1921 - Purchased by U.S. Army Signal Corps and converted into a cableship.
1924 - Loaded telegraph cable at the Woolwich factory of Siemens Bros. for Seattle/Alaska link.
1931 - Cable equipment scrapped and vessel returned to commercial use as a cannery ship for the Alaska Steamship Company.
1942 - Requisitioned for reconversion into a cableship. A sawmill winch was adapted into a cable winch, and from 1.1943 she laid over 300 n.m. of deep-sea telegraph cable, and much of the harbour defence cables for U.S. West coast and Alaskan ports.
19.7.1943 - Sank at Attu, Alaska.

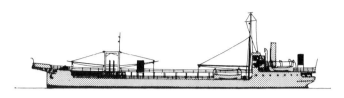

SILVERADO

US37. SILVERADO   2298 grt   245.6 x 42.0 x 24.1
E   Triple expansion, single screw.
CT (2), **BS** (3).
1918 - Completed by Long Beach Shipbuilding Company, California as engines-aft cargoship.
1943 - Requisitioned and converted into a cableship to replace *Dellwood* to maintain the Alaskan telegraph cables. Tall gantry connected the forward cable tank to the fo'c'stle.
c1950 - Taken out of service of the Alaska Communication System and broken up.

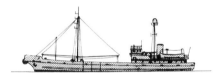

WILLIAM A. GLASSFORD
BASIL O. LENOIR

US38. WILLIAM A. GLASSFORD   575 grt   155.0 x 37.0 x 6.8
E   Diesel engines, triple screw, 9 knots.
CT (2), **BS** (3).
1943 - Completed by Seattle Shipbuilding & Drydock Co. as a self-propelled barge, her wooden hull was converted into a cableship for operation in the shallow waters of Alaska in the service of U.S. Army Signal Corps. Also used in Philippine waters.
1948 - Transferred to U.S. Navy renamed *Nashawena*. Cablelaying off California.
1952 - Placed in reserve.
1959 - Purchased by a West coast fishing company for charter to cable operating companies, renamed *Omega*.
1961 - Purchased by United States Underseas Cable Corporation for work on the Atlantic Underwater Test & Evaluation Centre, Bahamas. Under British flag, registered at Nassau 1962/64.
1964 - Refitted at Miami, moved to Pacific for cable duties.
10.1971 - Sold to International Marine Operations Inc.
1985 - Still operating as cableship *Omega* under the Panamanian flag.

US39. BASIL O. LENOIR   575 grt   155.0 x 37.0 x 6.8
E   Diesel engines, triple screw, 9 knots.
CT (2), **BS** (3).
1944 - Completed by Seattle Shipbuilding & Drydock Co. as a self-propelled barge, her wooden hull was converted into a cableship for operation in the shallow waters of Alaska in the service of U.S. Army Signal Corps. Sister of *William A. Glassford* and used post-war to maintain the Alaskan and Aleutian cables of the Alaska Communication System.
1956 - Laying of Seattle/Skagway coaxial telephone cable with *Albert J. Myer.* Cable jointly owned by Alaskan Communication System and A.T. & T.
1973 - After long service with the Alaskan Communication System, she was sold to the Radio Corporation of America.

US40. ELLERY W. NILES 840 grt   184.5 x 35.0 x 12.5
E   Diesel-electric propulsion, twin screw, 9 knots.
CT (1), **BS** (1).
1937 - Completed by Pusey & Jones, Wilmington(Delaware) as a mine planter for U.S. Army
1945 - Modified for cablelaying for U.S. Army Signal Corps.
1.1965 - Purchased by Marine Acoustical Services and converted into a cableship by the insertion of two cable tanks of total capacity 255 n.m., double drum winch and two bow sheaves and bow and stern thrusters were fitted. Renamed *F. V. Hunt.*
1978 - Converted into a salvage ship renamed *Cayman Salvage Master.*
2000 - Still in commission.

US41. SAMUEL MILLS(2) 885 grt   188.0 x 38.0 x 12.5
E   Reciprocating, twin screw, 9 knots.
CT (1), **BS** (1).
1942 - Completed by Marietta Shipyard, Point Pleasant(West Virginia) as a mine planter for U.S. Army.
1945 - Converted into a cableship for U.S. Army Signal Corps.
1960 - Converted to commercial use, renamed *Gran Canaria.*
1975 - Broken up.

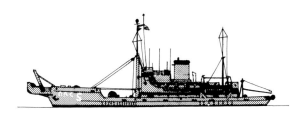

YAMACRAW

US42. YAMACRAW   1054 grt   216.0 x 34.2 x 18.0
E   Triple expansion, twin screw.
CT (1), **BS** (2), **SS** (1)
10.1942 - Completed by Marietta Shipyard, Point Pleasant(West Virginia) as a mine planter *Murray* for U.S. Army.
1.2.1944 - Sank off Cape Henry, Virginia after striking a mine.
1944 - Raised by U.S. Navy, repaired and commissioned as *Trapper.*

1948 - Transferred to U.S. Coastguard for cable repair duties renamed *Yamacraw*.
5.1959 - Handed back to U.S. Navy and used for the testing of devices in the underwater sound field. She was fitted with two electronics laboratories for acoustical research work. Pennant T-ARC 5.
7.1965 - Stricken from U.S. Navy and broken up in late 1967 by North American Smelting.

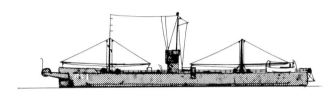

PORTUNUS

US43. PORTUNUS   743 grt   221.1 x 34.5 x 10.5
E   Direct drive diesels of 2800 bhp, twin screw.
CT (2), **BS** (2), **SS** (1).
1944 - Completed by Federal Shipbuilding & Drydock Co., Newark(NJ) as a landing craft.
1952 - Converted for cable repair work by U.S. Navy renamed *Portunus*.
11.1959 - Sold to Portuguese Navy and used as a diving tender renamed *Medusa*.

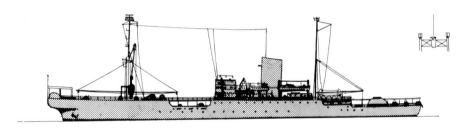

ALBERT J. MYER

US44. ALBERT J. MYER   3929 grt   334.0 x 47.1 x 30.8
E   Two reciprocating engines, twin screw, 15.5 knots.
CT (4) (three forward,one aft), **BS** (3), **SS** (1).
1946 - Completed by Pusey & Jones, Wilmington(Delaware) for U.S. Army as a S3-S2-BP1 type cableship and placed in reserve.
1952 - Commissioned by U.S. Army for cable work on Alaskan Communications System and for special projects of the U.S. Navy. Pennant T-ARC 6. Vessel named after first Chief Signal Officer, U.S. Army Signal Corps.
1966 - Transferred to U.S. Navy and steam cable machine replaced with electrical-driven version. Operated by Military Sealift Command.
3.1978 - 5.1980 - Rebuilt by Bethlehem Steel Corp., Key Highway Division, Baltimore. Modernisation including stripping the superstructure down to main deck level, gutting the hull, replacing the entire propulsion system & wiring & piping, and replacing the superstructure with aluminium where possible.
1995 - Deleted from U.S. Navy.

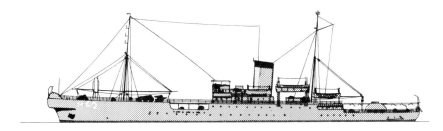

NEPTUNE

US45. NEPTUNE   3929 grt   334.0 x 47.1 x 30.8
E   Two reciprocating engines, twin screw, 15.5 knots.
CT (3), fourth tank aft converted into an auxiliary machinery room, **BS** (3), **SS** (1).
1946 - Completed by Pusey & Jones, Wilmington(Delaware) for U.S. Army as a S3-S2-BP1
type cableship *William H.G. Bullard* and placed in reserve.
1.6.1953 - Commissioned by U.S. Navy as cablelayer *Neptune* for laying of harbour defence
cables on the Eastern seaboard of U.S.A.   Original steam cable machinery replaced by
electrically-driven type by General Electric Corp. Pennant T-ARC 2. Helicopter platform fitted
aft.
11.1973 - Operated by Military Sealift Command.
2.1980-10.1982 - Modernised and rebuilt by General Dynamics Corp., Quincy(Mass.)
Modernisation including stripping the superstructure down to main deck level, gutting the hull,
replacing the entire propulsion system & wiring & piping, and replacing the superstructure
with aluminium where possible.
10.1991 - Placed in reserve.
1995 - Deleted from U.S. Navy.

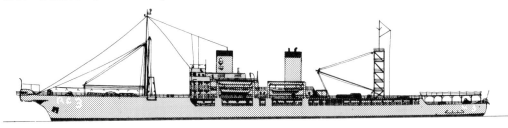

THOR, AEOLUS

US46. AEOLUS   7040 displacement   438.0 x 58.2 x 19.3
E   Turbo-electric propulsion, twin screw.
CT (3), **BS** (3).
1946 - Completed by Walsh Kaiser Corp., Providence as S4-SE2-BE5 attack cargoship and
laid-up.
14.5.1955 - Commissioned as *Aeolus* by U.S. Navy as cablelayer after conversion by
Bethlehem Steel Corp., Key Highway Division, Baltimore. Electrically-driven cable machinery
by General Electric Corp. Pennant T-ARC 3. Helicopter platform fitted aft.   Cable repair
facilities. Employed on cablelaying and hydrographic work.
1973 - Manned by Military Sealift Command.
1985 - Deleted from U.S. Navy.

US47. THOR   7040 displacement   438.0 x 58.2 x 19.3
E Turbo-electric propulsion, twin screw.
CT (3), **BS** (3).
1946 - Completed by Walsh Kaiser Corp., Providence as S4-SE2-BE5 attack cargoship and laid-up.
3.6.1956 - Commissioned as *Thor* by U.S. Navy as cablelayer after conversion by Bethlehem Steel Corp., Key Highway Division, Baltimore. Electrically-driven cable machinery by General Electric Corp. Pennant T-ARC 4. Helicopter platform fitted aft. Cable repair facilities. Employed on cablelaying and hydrographic work.
1973 - Manned by Military Sealift Command.
1979 - Deleted from U.S. Navy.

US48. ZEUS   8370 displacement   503.0 x 73.0 x 25.0
E Diesel-electric, twin screw. 5 diesel generators, 2 controllable pitch propellers, thrusters at bow and aft. Engine room remotely-controlled from bridge. 15.8 knots.
CT (4), **BS** (3), stern gantry.
7.1982 - Launched and 19.3.1984 completed by National Steel & Shipbuilding Corp. for U.S. Navy as dual purpose cablelayer/hydrographical research ship. Twin funnels aft. Complement of 89(51 crew, 6 U.S. Navy, 32 scientists). Pennant T-ARC7.
1984/2000 - Engaged in worldwide hydrographic surveys and cablelaying.

FRANCE.
I. FRENCH GOVERMENT

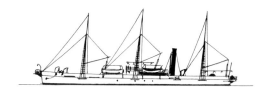

AMPERE(1)

FR1. AMPERE(1)   304 grt

E   Compound, single screw.

CT (1), **BS** (1).

1860 - Completed as *Dix Decembre* as a cargo ship.

1864 - Purchased by French Govt. and fitted out in England as a cableship by Siemens & Halske, renamed *Ampere* in 1870.

1864 - Oran/Cartagena telegraph cable.   (French Govt.)

1907 - Fitted with new cable machinery to maintain Anglo-French telegraph cables.

1925 - Broken up.

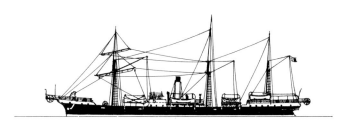

CHARENTE

FR2. CHARENTE   1061 grt   213.5 x 29.9 x 10.1

E   Compound, single screw.

CT (3), **BS** (2).

1862 - Completed in England as *Charente*.

1874 - Purchased by French Govt. and fitted out for cable work by Cie des Forges et Chantiers de la Seyne.

1893 - New cable machinery fitted.

1931 - Sold for scrap.

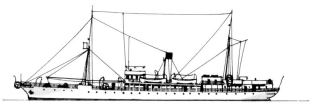

EMILE BAUDOT

FR3. EMILE BAUDOT   1049 grt   222.5 x 32.2 x 19.2

E   Triple expansion, twin screw, 9 knots. .

CT (3), **BS** (2).

1917 - Completed by Swan, Hunter & Wigham Richardson Ltd for French Govt. Based at Le Havre to maintain French coastal and Anglo - French telegraph cables.

1940/45 - Used for harbour defence cablelaying by Royal Navy, manned by Navy crew.

1945 - Handed back to French P.T.T. at Gibraltar.

1945/62 - Based at Brest maintaining French end of Transatlantic and Anglo/French cables.

1962 - Broken up.

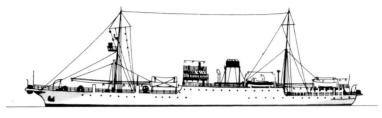

AMPERE(2)

FR4. AMPERE(2)   2434 grt   300.4 x 41.1 x 23.7

E   Triple expansion, twin screw.

CT (3), **BS** (3), **SS** (1).

1930 - Completed by Ste Provencale, La Ciotat for French P.T.T. as a cableship based at La Seyne maintaining the Mediterranean network of telegraph cables, and also the Brest/ Casablanca/Dakar cable.

1930/40 - New cables laid between Marseilles/North Africa.

1942 - Used as a naval auxiliary by German Navy.

1944 - Scuttled in Marseilles harbour.

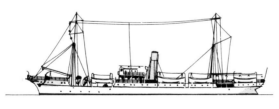

ARAGO

FR5. ARAGO   901 grt   208.4 x 30.1 x 16.6

E   Triple expansion, single screw.

CT (3), **BS** (2).

1914 - Completed by Goole Shipbuilding & Repairing Co. Ltd for Eastern Telegraph Company as *Transmitter*.

1914 - She made three repairs to the Porthcurno/Vigo cable on her way out to West Africa.

1914 - Freetown/Accra   (African Direct Telegraph Co.)

1932 - Sold to French Govt. P.T.T. renamed *Arago*. Based at Dakar maintaining the French West African network of cables of Cie des Cables Sud Americains.

1944/45 - Reinstated Mediterranean cables.
1946 - Sold and employed on the clearance work in Toulon harbour.
1950 - Broken up.

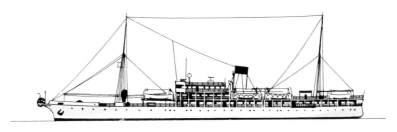

ALSACE

FR6. ALSACE   2092 grt   288.9 x 39.9 x 17.6
E Triple expansion, twin screw, 14.5 knots.
CT (3), **BS** (2).
1939 - Completed by Chantiers et Ateliers de St. Nazaire for French P.T.T.
1940 - Laid-up at Algiers after German occupation of France.
1942 - Stationed at Dakar to relieve *Arago*.
1946/74 - Stationed at La Seyne for maintenance of French Mediterranean cables.
9.1974 - Sold for scrap to N.V. Rijsdijk and broken up at Hendrik-Ido-Ambacht.

FR7. PIERRE PICARD   See *Edouard Jeramec* FR15

FR8. INGENIEUR en chef HANFF   199 grt   117.9 x 22.2 x 7.6
E Oil engine of 200 bhp, single screw, 8.5 knots.
CT (2), **BS** (2).
1937 - Completed by Kremer & Son, Elmshorn as *Elveshorn* for Elmshorner D/S A.G., Hamburg. Chartered by Norddeutsche Seekabelwerke on a number of occasions for short lays and repair work, and engaged on cable work throughout WWII.
19.1.1946 - Handed over to Netherlands P.T.T. for repair of their coastal and river cables renamed *Poolster* in 1949.
6.1949 - Handed over to French P.T.T. renamed *Ingenieur en chef Hanff*, and used for the maintenance of the French domestic network of cables.
1964 - Sold for commercial trading, renamed *Le Majungais*.
1966 - Resumed coastal cablelaying for French P.T.T. renamed *Ingenieur en chef Hanff*.
1970 - Returned to commercial trading, renamed *Le Majungais*.
1999 - Owned by Armement Maritime Lewis, Madagascar.
2000 - Still in commission.

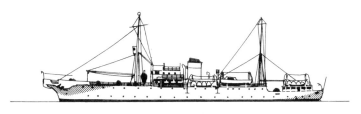

D'ARSONVAL

FR9. D'ARSONVAL   1558 displacement   247.2 x 33.7 x 12.7
E Triple expansion, twin screw, 16 knots. 90 crew.
CT (2), **BS** (2), **SS** (2).
1929 - Completed by Breda Company as *Giasone*(2) at their Marghera(Venice) yard for Italian Govt. as a combined cableship/boom defence/salvage ship/auxiliary for use by Italian Navy.
1943 - Captured by Germany at Genoa.
1945 - Found sunk in Marseilles at end of the war, refloated and taken over by French Govt. renamed *D'Arsonval* based at Brest.
28.2.1965 - Arrived Antwerp for scrapping.

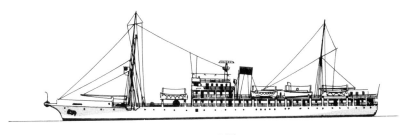

AMPERE(3)

FR10. AMPERE(3)   2100 grt   299.0 x 41.4 x 16.9
E Turbine-powered 2500 shp, twin screw, variable pitch propellers.
CT (3), **BS** (2).
1951 - Completed by Chantiers de Normandie, Grand Quevilly for French P.T.T. and based at La Seyne for maintenance of French Mediterranean cables.
1958 - Laid half of the Anglo-French power cables across the English Channel with *Dame Caroline Haslett* laying the other half.
1985 - Broken up.

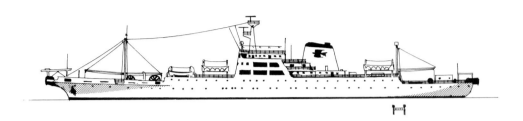

MARCEL BAYARD

FR11. MARCEL BAYARD   4500 grt   387.1 x 51.3 x 21.6
E   Diesel-electric propulsion, twin screw.
CT (4), **BS** (2), **SS** (1).
29.6.1961 - Launched & 1961 - completed by Chanties et Ateliers Augustin Normand, Le Havre. Named after former Chief Engineer of French P.T.T. Submarine Cable Department. Crew of 106 officers, men and cable technicians. Ice strengthened, range of 55 days, used in conjunction with *Jean Charcot,* 2110/65, an oceanographic survey ship, which mapped cable routes for the French P.T.T.
6.1.1981 - On fire in engine room & sank at La Seyne at her berth.
1.7.1981 - Refloated, completely gutted.
20.10.1981 - Left Toulon in tow for Valencia for breaking up.

II. COMMERCIAL CABLESHIPS

POUYER-QUERTIER

FR12. POUYER-QUERTIER   1396 grt   238.2 x 35.9 x 22.9
E   Compound, twin screw.
CT (2), **BS** (2), **SS** (1).
1879 - Completed by Charles Mitchell & Co., Newcastle for Cie Francaise du Telegraphiques de Paris a New York. Designed by Sir William Siemens on similar lines to *Faraday*(1) with twin screws, bow rudder and swivelling bow & stern sheaves. Monsieur Pouyer-Quertier was the founder and director of the company, commonly known as 'P-Q'.
1879/90 - Based at Le Havre maintaining the Atlantic telegraph cables of the company, one of which had an intermediate landfall at Porthcurno, Cornwall.
1895 - Transfer to Cie Francaise des Cables Telegraphiques.

1896 - Moved to West Indies on the introduction of *Contre Amiral Caubet* and laid an extension of the Venezuelan cable from Willemstad(Curacao)/Coro(Venezuela).
1931 - Broken up.

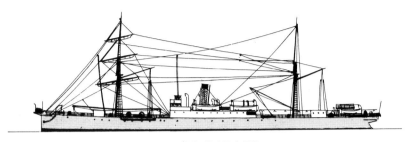

FRANCOIS ARAGO

FR13. FRANCOIS ARAGO   3342 grt   320.0 x 42.4 x 28.0
E Compound, single screw.
CT (4), **BS** (2)
11.1882 - Completed by Sunderland Shipbuilding Company for the New Zealand trade as *Westmeath* for R. M. Hudson, Sunderland.
1887/89 - Chartered by W. T. Henley to lay cables in the West Indies for Soc. Francaise des Telegraphiques Sous-Marins.
1890 - Halifax/Bermuda telegraph cable.
1893 - Purchased by Soc. Indutrielle des Telephones renamed *Francois Arago*.
1914 - Sold out of the cable world to Cie Francaise de Marine et de Commerce renamed *Peronne*. Lost during WWI.

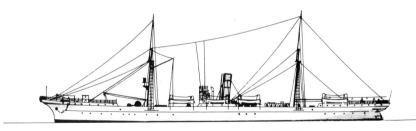

CONTRE AMIRAL CAUBET

FR14. CONTRE AMIRAL CAUBET   2078 grt   323.8 x 34.8 x 26.2
E Compound, single screw.
CT (3), **BS** (2)
1875 - Completed by Forges et Chantiers de la Mediterranean, Le Havre as *Portena* for Chargeurs Reunis, Havre.
1896 - Purchased by Cie Francaise des Cables Telegraphiques and fitted out for cable work renamed *Contre Amiral Caubet*.
1896/1915 - Based at Le Havre as a repair ship.
1915 - Sold for commercial work to Junius H. Stone, New York renamed *Vigo*.
1919 - Broken up.

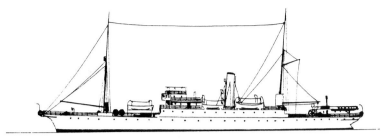

EDOUARD JERAMEC

FR15. EDOUARD JERAMEC   2316 grt   289.2 x 41.1 x 23.7
E   Triple expansion, twin screw.
CT (3), **BS** (2), **SS** (1).
1913 - Completed by Forges et Chantiers de Grayville for Cie Francaise des Cables Telegraphiques as a repair ship for North Atlantic cables based at Le Havre.
1929 - Sold to All America Cables and after a refit was engaged on the maintenance of the New York/Colon cables. Name unchanged.
1946 - Sold to French Govt. P.T.T. renamed *Pierre Picard* for repair of the French Atlantic cables including those of the vessel's first owners, whose cables were taken over by the P.T.T. in 1945.
1948 - Refitted & converted to oil-burning, and undertook the reconditioning of the Brest/Cape Cod cable.
19.12.1952 - Sank in Brest harbour.

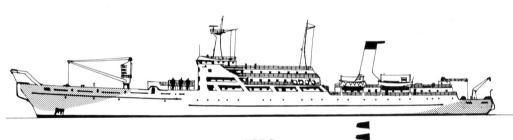

VERCORS

FR16. VERCORS   5886 grt   433.0 x 59.5 x 24.0
E   Diesel-electric propulsion, twin screw, 16.9 knots.
CT (3), **BS** (2).
1975 - Completed by Soc. Nouvelle des Ateliers & Chantiers du Havre for France Cables & Radio. 115 crew. One of the first ships to be fitted with a plough launched by an 'A' frame over the stern for cable burial and protection from trawling.
1975 - Maiden voyage on French Mediterranean coast St. Rapael/La Foux coaxial 19 n.m.
1975 - Perpignan/Bizerta coaxial   501 n.m. & 47 repeaters.
1976 - Marseilles/Palo(Italy)   371 n.m. & 81 repeaters.
1976 - TAT6 Rhode Island/St. Hiliaire(France) coaxial, laid both shore ends.
1976 - Eastbourne/Courseulles coaxial 108 n.m. & 27 repeaters.
1977 - Bastia(Corsica)/Marseilles 181 n.m. & 42 repeaters.

1977 - Casablanca/Dakar/Abidjan(Ivory Coast) 2875 n.m. & 246 repeaters - a connection was made to the French P.T.T. cables at Casablanca.

1978 - Eastbourne/St. Valery coaxial 57 n.m. & 21 repeaters.

1978 - Tetuan(Morocco)/Marseilles 825 n.m. & 168 repeaters.

1980/99 - Worldwide cablelaying on contract including the SEA-ME-WE3 system in the Far East.

2000 - Still in commission.

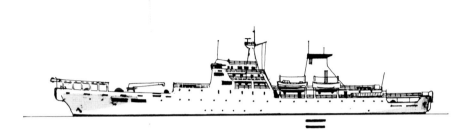

LEON THEVENIN, RAYMOND CROZE

FR17. LEON THEVENIN   4845 grt   107.8 x 17.8 x 9.0

E   Diesel-electric propulsion, three Crepelle 8-cylinder driving 3 generators connected to 2 electric motors, twin screw. 15 knots. 2 thrusters.

CT (3), **BS** (2), **SS** (1)

1983 - Completed by Soc. Nouvelles Ats. & Chants. du Havre for Cie Francaise Cables Sous-Marins & Radio Paris, later France Telecom. Based at Brest, and was a 'host' ship for the submersible *Scarab*.

2000 - Still in commission.

FR18. RAYMOND CROZE   4845 grt   107.8 x 17.8 x 9.0

E   Diesel-electric propulsion, three Crepelle 8-cylinder driving 3 generators connected to 2 electric motors, twin screw. 15 knots. 2 thrusters.

CT (3), **BS** (2), **SS** (1)

1983 - Completed by Soc. Nouvelles Ats. & Chants. de la Rochelle-Pallice for Cie Francaise Cables Sous-Marins & Radio Paris, later France Telecom. Based at Toulon.

2000 - Still in commission.

FR19, FR20, FR21 --------------   8200 dwt

E   Diesel-electric propulsion

5500 tonnes cable capacity, stern working

2001 - Due for completion by Hyundai Mipo Dockyard, S. Korea for joint ownership of Alcatel Submarine Networks and Louis Dreyfus. Alcatel, a French telecomms pioneer since 1872, purchased the European telecomms activities of American-owned I.T.T. Group in 1987, including the British subsidiary Standard Telephones & Cables Ltd (S.T.C.) of Southampton and Greenwich, to form Alcatel Submarine Networks. An option exists for a fourth vessel.

JAPAN.
1. JAPANESE GOVERNMENT.

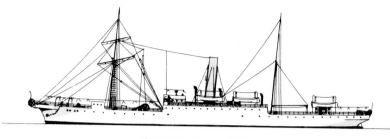

OKINAWA MARU

JP1. OKINAWA MARU   2232 grt   307.2 x 40.1 x 13.5
E   Triple expansion, twin screw, 11 knots.
CT (3), **BS** (3), **SS** (1)
1896 - Completed by Lobnitz & Co., Renfrew for Japanese Government as their first cableship, based at Tokyo. Japan had been connected by submarine telegraph cable in 1871 by the Great Northern Telegraph Company, and all international connections had then been maintained by this Danish company and the Commercial Pacific Cable Company. By the turn of the century, all of the main Japanese islands had been connected with over 2,000 nautical miles of cable, and the Japanese Government began to participate more actively.
4.1938 - Withdrawn from service.

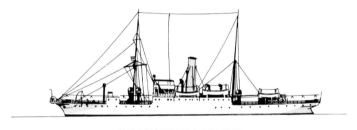

OGASAWARA MARU

JP2. OGASAWARA MARU   1460 grt   240.0 x 34.0 x 12.5
E   Triple expansion, twin screw, 11 knots.
CT (3), **BS** (3), **SS** (1).
1906 - Completed by Mitsubishi Dockyard, Nagasaki for Japanese Govt. as first cableship built in Japan. Based at Tokyo for the Ministry of Communications.
22.8.1945 - Withdrawn from service.

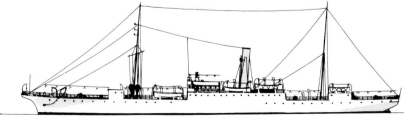

NANYO MARU

JP3. NANYO MARU   3605 grt   344.6 x 44.0 x 30.3

E Triple expansion, twin screw, 11 knots.

CT (4), **BS** (3), **SS** (1).

1925 - Completed by Osaka Iron Works for Japanese Govt. and based at Nagasaki for the Ministry of Communications.

20.2.1944 - War loss.

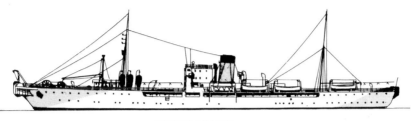

TOYO MARU

JP4. TOYO MARU   3718 grt   347.4 x 48.4 x 25.4

E Geared turbine of 3600 shp, twin screw, 14 knots.

CT (4), **BS** (3), **SS** (1).

1937 - Completed by Kawasaki Dockyard, Kobe for Japanese Govt and based at Tokyo for the Ministry of Communications. Her turbine machinery was a novelty in cableships, which call for very slow working speeds and close manoeuvrability - for the latter an electrically-driven Voith-Schneider bow propeller was fitted.

6.7.1945 - War loss.

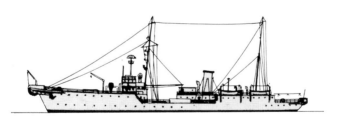

TSURUSHIMA MARU

JP5. TSURUSHIMA MARU   1176 grt   239.4 x 35.5 x 12.0

E Triple expansion, twin screw, 14 knots.

CT (2), **BS** (2), **SS** (1)

1940 - Completed by Kawasaki Heavy Industries, Kobe as *Tsurushima* for Japanese Navy, fitted with five small guns and for minelaying over the stern. She had three sisters *Hashima*, *Otate* and *Tateishi* that were lost in the war.

1945 - Ren. *Tsurushima Maru* in the service of the Ministry of Communications.

1968 - Broken up.

OSEI MARU

JP6. OSEI MARU   641 grt   160.7 x 27.9 x 13.9
E   Akasaka oil engine of 550 bhp, single screw, 10 knots.
CT (2), **BS** (3), **SS** (1)
1941 - Completed by Makata Dockyard, Osaka as a three-hold engine amidships motor coaster.
9.1946 - Taken over by Japanese Govt. for cable work and fitted with 3 bow sheaves and 1 stern sheave. Based at Osaka with a cruising range of 2,000 nautical miles.
31.3.1953 - Sold out of the cable world to Sank Shosen K. K. name unchanged.
1957 - Sold to Kita Kyushu Kisen K.K. and broken up around 1960.

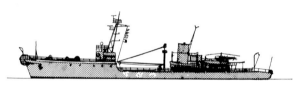

TSUGARU

JP7. TSUGARU   1000 grt   216.5 x 34.1 x 11.0
E   Diesel engines of 3200 bhp, twin screw, 13 knots.
CT (1), **BS** (2), **SS** (1)
1955 - Completed by Shin Mitsibish Jyuko Co. for Japanese Navy as a combined minelayer/cableship.
7.1969 - 4.1970 - Converted into a full cableship for Japanese Maritime Defence Agency by Nippon Steel Tube Company. In addition, the Japanese Govt. used around six coastal cableships of around 100 grt from WWII onwards for laying short cables in the Inland Sea.

II. CABLESHIPS OWNED BY CABLE OWNERS.

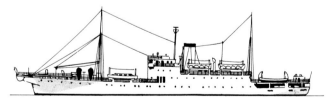

CHIYODA MARU

JP8. CHIYODA MARU   1849 grt   268.1 x 38.1 x 17.4
E Double compound expansion, twin screw, 10 knots.
CT (3), **BS** (2).
1948 - Completed by Mitsubishi Heavy Industries for Nippon T. & T. Corp and based at Tokyo. Her name is derived from the Chiyoda-ku district of Tokyo, where the submarine cable plant of Nippon T. & T. is based.
1975 - Transferred to Nippon Denshin Denwa.
1979 - Broken up in Japan.

JP9. SETO MARU   219 grt   121.6 x 22.4 x 6.4
E B. & W. Alpha type diesel of 360 bhp, single screw, 9 knots.
CT (1), **BS** (2).
1956 - Completed by Nipponkai Heavy Industries, Toyama for Nippon T. & T. Corp.
1975 - Transferred to Nippon Denshin Denwa.
9.1979 - Broken up in Japan.

JP10. AMAKUSA MARU   359 grt   144.6 x 24.9 x 13.1
E Diesel engine of 950 bhp, single screw, 11 knots.
CT (2), **BS** (1).
1961 - Completed to a trawler design for Nippon T. & T. Corp and based at Tokyo.
1975 - Transferred to Nippon Denshin Denwa.
12.1983 - Demolition commenced in Japan at Sasebo, Nagasaki.

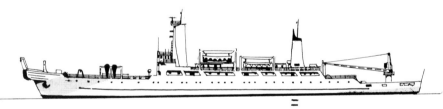

KDD MARU

JP11. KDD MARU   4299 grt   373.6 x 50.6 x 20.8
E Twin Mitsubishi 6-cylinder diesels each of 2200 bhp, twin screw, 16 knots.
CT (3), **BS** (3), **SS** (1).
25.2.1967 - Launched and 6.1967 completed by Mitsubishi Heavy Industries, Shimonoseki for Kokusai Cableship K.K. - a subsidiary of Kokusai Denshin Denwa (K.D.D.). Used for laying & repairing of global networks connected to Japan. Based at Yokohama.
1992 - With the delivery of *KDD Ocean Link, KDD Maru* was relegated to a repair ship only.
18.12.1997 - Demolition commenced in Japan.

JP12. TSUGARU MARU   1662 grt   277.5 x 41.4 x 15.1
E Direct drive diesel of 3,000 bhp, 13.5 knots.
CT (1), **BS** (2).
1969 - Completed by Mitsubishi Heavy Industries for Nippon T. & T. Corp. and based at Yokohama. 60 crew.
1969 - Laid first Japanese domestic coaxial telephone system with repeaters on maiden voyage.

1975 - Transferred to Nippon Denshin Denwa.
1993 - Broken up in Japan.

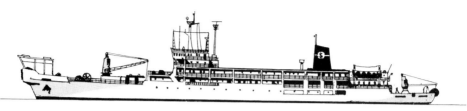

KUROSHIO MARU

JP13. KUROSHIO MARU   4776 grt   391.4 x 53.2 x 18.4
E Direct drive 16-cylinder MAN diesel of 8900 bhp, controllable pitch propeller, 16.5 knots.
CT (3), **BS** (3), **SS** (2).
1975 - Completed by Mitsubishi Heavy Industries, Shimonoseki for Nippon T. & T. Corp. as
the largest cableship built at the time in Japan. Based at Yokohama and duties include
oceanographic research. Fitted with a plough for cable burying down to 100 fathoms, lifted
out over stern by special electric crane.
1975 - Okinawa/Kagoshima (southern tip of Kyushu) coaxial. Shore ends laid by small
chartered craft.
1999 - Owned by K.K. Nagashima, Tokyo.

JP14. SETOUCHI MARU   822 grt   64.7 x 11.3 x 3.5
E   Two 6-cylinder 4SCSA oil engines geared to two screw shafts, 12 knots.
CT (2), **BS** (2), **SS** (1)
1979 - Completed by Koyo Dockyard for Nippon Denshin Denwa (Japan Telegraph &
Telephone) with two decks including a separate through deck for cable handling.
1999 - Still in commission.

KDD OCEAN LINK of 1992

JP15. KDD OCEAN LINK   9510 grt   133.0 x 19.6 x 9.0

E Four 6-cylinder Daihatsu oil engines of 8800 bhp, twin screw, 15 knots.

CT (3), **BS** (2), **SS** (1) Cable capacity 2650 cu. metres, 2 Drum type bow cable engines, trencher and 'A' frame with a lift of 25 tons.

1992 - Completed by Mitsubishi Heavy Industries, Shimonoseki for Kokusai Cableship K.K. Based at Yokohama with a crew of 85 as one of their two main cable layers.

1992 - Laid TPC4 optical fibre North America/Japan.

1992 - Laid Chikura/Miyazaki optical fibre cable.

1993 - Laid Asian Pacific Cable (APC) optical fibre cable.

JP16. KDD PACIFIC LINK   7764 grt   93.9 x 20.5 x 7.5

E Six Normo 9-cylinder oil engines driving generators connected to electric motors, twin screw. 13 knots.

CT (3), **SS** (2)

1993 - Completed by Singmarine Dockyard & Eng. Pte., Singapore as offshore well-stimulation vessel *Western Renaissance*.

1997 - Converted to a cablelayer for KCS Panama Inc, Panama and chartered to Kokusai Cableship K.K. Based at Yokohama as one of their two main cablelayers.

JP17. KOYO MARU   1336 grt   74.25 x 12.5 x 7.0

E Four Daihatsu 6-cylinder oil engines of 3000 bhp, twin screw, 13.5 knots.

CT (2), **SS** (2)

1984 - Completed by Mitsubishi Heavy Industries, Shimonoseki for Nippon Denshin Denwa Kosha (Japan Telegraph & Telephone Corp.), Tokyo. Based at Yokohama. Two decks with separate deck for cable handling.

JP18. KOUSHIN MARU   2828 grt   74.88 x 16.5 x 7.5

E Two Yanmar 6-cylinder oil engines driving 2 generators connected to 2 electric motors. 3800 bhp. 12 knots. 2 thrusters.

CT (2), **SS** (2)

1998 - Completed by Hitachi Zosen, Kanagawa Works, Kawasaki for Dokai Tugboat Co. Ltd, Kitakyushu, Fukuoka.

GERMANY.

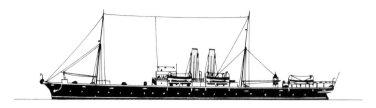

VON   PODBIELSKI

GE1. VON PODBIELSKI   1494 grt   265.5 x 35.1 x 22.4
E Triple expansion, twin screw, 13 knots.
CT (3), **BS** (2), **SS** (1).
1899 - Completed by D. J. Dunlop & Co., Port Glasgow to a British design for Norddeutshe Seekabelwerke, formed in 5.1899 with a new factory at Nordenham on the Weser to make Government-owned telegraph cables.
1900 - Shanghai/Tsingtau assisted by *Sherard Osborn, Store Nordiske*(1)
1901 - Emden/Borkum/Bacton   (Norddeutsche Seekabelwerke)
1903/04 - Assisted *Stephan* on Emden/Azores/ New York   (German Atlantic Tel. Co.)
1905 - Constantza/Constantinople   (Eastern European Tel. Co.)
1905 - Sold to Netherlands East Indies Govt. renamed *Telegraaf*
1905 - Balikpapan/Macassar   (Neth. East Indies Govt.)
1914 - Broken up, replaced by *Zuiderkruis*.

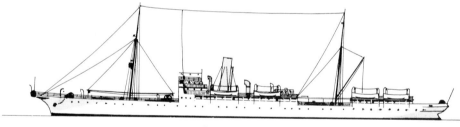

STEPHAN

GE2. STEPHAN   4630 grt   391.8 x 48.3 x 29.8
E Triple expansion, twin screw, 14 knots.
CT (4), **BS** (3), **SS** (1).
29.12.1902 - Launched and 3.1903 completed by Stettiner Vulkan for Norddeutscher Seekabelwerke as the first German-built layer/repairer.
1903/04 - Emden/Azores/New York assisted by *Von Podbielski* (German Atlantic Tel. Co.)
1904/05 - Celebes/Yap/Guam & Yap/Menado/Shanghai   (German-Neth. Tel. Co.)
1906 - Cuxhaven/Arendal   (German Govt./Norwegian PTT)
1907 - Moen/Liepaja/St. Petersburg   (Gt. Northern Tel. Co.)
1908 - Trieste/Pola/Sebenike   (Italian Govt.)
1908/11 - Borkum/Tenerife/Monrovia/Pernambuco   (German South American Tel.Co)
1910 - Trieste/Pola/Split   (Italian Govt.)
1911 - Monrovia/Conakry/Grand Bassam   (French Govt.)
1911 - Monrovia/Lome/Duala(Cameroons)   (German South American Tel.Co)
1912 - Balboa/San Elena   (Central & Sth American Tel. Co)

1913 - Nordeney/Mundesley   (German & U.K. G.P.O.)
1913 - Balikpapan/Soerabaja & Kema/Ternato   (Neth. East Indies Govt.)
9.1914 - Took refuge in Vigo for the duration of the war.
11.1918 - Handed over to Americans for a short while before being ceded to Britain.
1919 - Purchased by Telcon.
1923 - Key West/Havana telephone cable   (A.T. & T.)
192 - Miami/Cuba   (All America Cables)
1926 - Sold for breaking up.

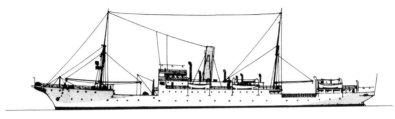

GROSSHERZOG von OLDENBURG

GE3. GROSSHERZOG von OLDENBURG   2691 grt   304.2 x 41.7 x 25.5
E   Triple expansion, twin screw, 12 knots.
CT (3), **BS** (3), **SS** (1).
21.10.1905 - Launched and 1.1906 completed by F. Schichau & Co., Danzig for Norddeutsche Seekabelwerke.
1919 - Ceded to Italy as war reparations renamed *Citta di Milano*(2).
1924/25 - Laid parts of the Italcable system from Italy to Spain/Canaries/Cape Verde Islands and South America. During the inter-war years she filled in with many other duties e.g. Arctic exploration.
6.1943 - Escaped take over by Germany on surrender of Italy.
18.9.1943 - Scuttled at Savona.

NORDENEY

GE4. NORDENEY   1460   233.0 x 34.4 x 17.5
E   Triple expansion, twin screw, 11 knots.
CT (3), **BS** (2)
1915 - Completed by Howaldtswerke, Kiel as an oil tanker for the German Navy.
1922 - Converted into a cableship by Deutsche Werke, Rustringen for Norddeutsche Seekabelwerke.
1945 - Ceded to Britain and renamed *Alert*(3) (q.v.) by U.K.G.P.O.

GE5. NEPTUN(1)   7481 grt   434.3 x 57.3 x 32.2
E   Triple expansion, twin screw. 11 knots.
CT (4), **BS** (3), **SS** (1).
1926 - Completed by Blohm & Voss, Hamburg for Norddeutsche Seekabelwerke as a dual-purpose oil tanker/cableship.
1926 - Borkum/Fayal(Azores)   (German Atlantic Tel. Co.)
1926 - Aldeburgh/Domburg assisted by *Nordeney*   (U.K.G.P.O.)
1930 - Key West/Havana coaxial telephone cable   (A. T. & T.)
1934 - Pilau/Gross Mollen
1945 - Ceded to U.K. as war reparations & sold to Hector Whaling Ltd renamed *Thule* for use as a whale oil tanker and supply ship, cable machinery & bow and stern sheaves removed.
1959 - After loss of *Ocean Layer* she was considered by Submarine Cables Ltd for reconversion into a cableship, not proceeded with.
19.1.1961 - Arrived Antwerp for breaking up.

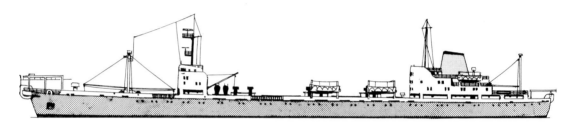

NEPTUN(2)

GE6. NEPTUN(2)   8910 grt   493.9 x 61.8 x 29.5
E   Diesel or diesel-electric propulsion, twin screw.
CT (5), **BS** (3), **SS** (1).
1962 - Completed by Lubecker Flenderwerke A.G. for Union Kabellgungs & Schiffarts as a dual-purpose cableship/bulk carrier. She had a very large cable capacity with five of her six holds used to stow cable with the sixth used for grapnels, grappling wire & buoys. An earlier scheme in 1959 to purchase a cargoship built by the Furness Shipbuilding Co. Ltd on Teesside in 1955 was subsequently abandoned by Union Kabellgungs & Schiffarts.
1963 - Eastern Test range cable system   (U.S.A.F.)
1964 - Philippines/Vietnam   (U.S.A.F.)
1.1965 - Sold to United States Undersea Cable Corporation, name unchanged. She had just laid the Philippines/Vietnam cables under charter from her German owner, and she remained in the Philippines as guardship until recalled to U.S.A. to load the Johnston Island cable in 1966.
1966/67 - Vietnamese coastal cables & Saigon/Bangkok extension, remained in these waters as guardship for these cables.
1971 - Taiwan/Okinawa   (U.S. Govt.)
10.1971 - Sold to International Marine Operations Inc, a subsidiary of the I.T.T. Group and took over as guardship for U.S. Pacific military cables.
12.1975 - Sold to Cable & Wireless Ltd and 6.1977 renamed *Cable Venture* (q.v.)

GE7. KABEL-JAU   500 grt   162.5 x 29.9 x 13.6

E Diesel engine 350 bhp, single screw, 8 knots.

CT (1), **BS** (2)

1944 - Completed as coaster *Tessy* by Kalmar Varv., renamed *Delfin* in 1957 and reverted to *Tessy* in 1961.

1966 - Purchased by Norddeutsche Seekabelwerke and renamed *Kabel-Jau*, fitted with permanent bow sheaves and cable machinery located just behind the fo'c'stle. She was their last permanent cablelayer.

1971 - Sold out of the cable world and deleted from Lloyd's register by 1974.

GE8. MANTA   2723 grt   81.4 x 16.3 x 4.9

E Two Sulzer 6-cylinder oil engines by Cegielski.

CT (2), **SS** (2)

1992 - Completed by Stocznia Szczecinska, Szczecin as oil rig supply vessel *Peteka Supply II*, having been launched as the Russian *Neftegaz 93*.

1993 - Sold to Hermann Buss K.G. Gmbh, Leer and converted to a cableship for oil related work, renamed *Manta* in 1995. Ice-strengthened.

DENMARK.

H.C. OERSTED

DE1. H.C. OERSTED   749 grt   178.1 x 26.6 x 15.1
E   Compound, single screw.
CT (3), **BS** (2), **SS** (1).
1872 - Completed by Burmeister & Wain, Copenhagen for Great Northern Telegraph Company as the world's first purpose-built and purpose-designed cable repair ship. She spent her life repairing cables in European and Far Eastern waters for the important telegraph lines of Vladivostock/Nagasaki/Shanghai. Named after the discoverer of electromagnetism.
1922 - Sold for breaking up in Copenhagen.

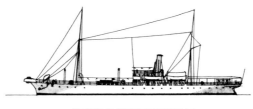

STORE NORDISKE(1)

DE2. STORE NORDISKE(1)   882 grt   192.0 x 29.1 x 13.5
E   Compound, single screw.
CT (3), **BS** (2).
1880 - Completed by Burmeister & Wain, Copenhagen for Great Northern Telegraph Company. All of her repair work was done in the Far East and she was frequently chartered to the Japanese Government.
1900/01 - Woosung/Tschifu; Fusan/Tsuschima/Taku; Tschifu/Wei-Hai-Wei; Tsingtau/Tschifu
1905 - Yangtze shore end of Yap/Shanghai assisting *Stephan* (Norddeutsche Seekabelwerke)
1906 - Yangtze shore end of Manila/Shanghai assisting *Silvertown* (Comm. Cable Co.)
1923 - Sold for breaking up in Shanghai.

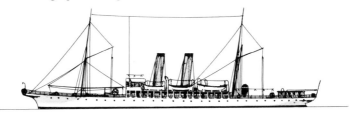

PACIFIC

DE3. PACIFIC   1570 grt   264.6 x 35.8 x 21.5
E Triple expansion, twin screw, 12 knots.
CT (3), **BS** (3), **SS** (1).
1903 - Completed by Burmeister & Wain, Copenhagen for the Great Northern Telegraph Company. All of her repair work was done on the Far Eastern cable network. She was partly owned by the Eastern Telegraph Company of Great Britain, for whom she also did cable repair work in the Far East.
11.1941 - Moved from Japanese waters and worked in Indian Ocean and Persian Gulf for the Allies.
1950 - Broken up at Bombay.

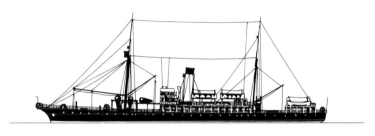

EDOUARD SUENSON

DE4. EDOUARD SUENSON   1560 grt   260.0 x 35.5 x 16.6
E Triple expansion, single screw.
CT (3), **BS** (2).
1922 - Completed by Royal Danish Dockyard, Copenhagen for Great Northern Telegraph Company. All of her repair work was done in European waters. Named after the company's Far Eastern manager, who spent his entire career in China, Japan and the Far East.
1922 - Repairing the company's European cables, particularly Newbiggin/Sondervig.
1948 - Laid Danish mainland/Bornholm cable.
1950 - Laid Weymouth/Fano coaxial telephone cable assisted by *Monarch*(4).
1960 - Copenhagen/Bornholm/Mielno(Poland) coaxial shore ends.
1963 - SCOTICE shore ends at Prins Christians Sund, Greenland.
12.9.1968 - Arrived for breaking up at Masnedo, Denmark.

DE5. STORE NORDISKE(2)   1462 grt   264.0 x 35.2 x 16.8
E Triple expansion, single screw.
CT· (3), **BS** (3).
1922 - Completed by A/S Nakskovskibs, Nakskov for Great Northern Telegraph Company.
11.1941 - Moved from Japanese waters and worked in Indian Ocean and Persian Gulf.
1948/50 - Extensive repairs to Vladivostock/Nagasaki cable to allow it to be re-opened, the remaining Far Eastern cables were not restored.
1964 - Surveyed route of Hawaii/Johnston Island defence cable for U.S.A.F.
1969 - Sold to Mitsui Ocean Development & Eng. Co. renamed *Ohtaka*.
8.4.1970 - Serious fire at Yokosuka while fitting out for oceanographic work.
4.1972 - Taken out of service and broken up.

DE6. C.E. KRARUP(2)   252 grt   102.0 x 24.7 x 10.7
E Oil engine, single screw.
CT (1), electrically-driven cable machinery.
1941 - Completed by A/S Nakskovskibs, Nakskov for Danish Govt. P.T.T. with a crew of 16.
She replaced a wooden launch of the same name of length 40 feet and in commission from
1925 to 1930.
1962 - Sold out of the cable world as a training ship, renamed *Navigator*.
1999 - Owned by Ivar Kristian Tang, Copenhagen.

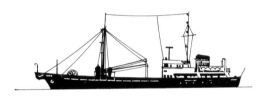

PETER FABER(2)

DE7. PETER FABER(2)   499 grt   184.1 x 31.3 x 10.9
E Alpha diesel, single screw, 12 knots.
CT (1) for carrying cable on drums, **BS** (2).
1961 - Completed by A/S Svendborg Skibsverft, Svendborg for Danish Govt. P.T.T.   She
replaced a small wooden sailing ship of length 49 feet of the same name in commission
between 1913 and 1946, which was particularly useful in the mine-strewn waters off Denmark
during WWII. Based at Korsor with a crew of 17.
1982 - Replaced by *Peter Faber*(3) and renamed *Faber*.
1983 - Sold to Greek Govt. (Hellenic Telecomms Organization) and renamed *Thalis*.
1999 - Still in commission.

NORTHERN sailing from the Tyne in 1986 with
CABLE VENTURE in background at right. (Author)

DE8. NORTHERN   1769 grt   268.6 x 40.4 x 18.0
E Diesel. Single controllable pitch propeller.
CT (3), **BS** (3).
1962 - Completed by Bijkers Aannemingsbedrijf, Gorinchen for J. Lauritzen, Copenhagen as *Sirpa Dan*.
7.1968 - Converted to a cableship, the third such conversion for the Great Northern Telegraph Company, renamed *Northern*. Two earlier conversions at the beginning of WWII had been made to the cargoships *Kabel* 720/18 and *Karla* 941/20 for maintenance of the company's cables in Europe. Northern's manoeuvrability was helped by installing a bow thruster.
1968/88 - Employed repairing company's Far Eastern cables including a coaxial telephone cable laid by *KDD Maru* from Nakhodka (USSR) to Sekiyama(Japan) on charter.
1988 - Sold to Cable & Wireless(Marine) Ltd name unchanged, arrived on the Bermuda station during 4.1989.
1990 - Converted into an oceanographical survey ship for a joint venture by Cable & Wireless (Marine) Ltd and Wimpole, renamed *Ocean Surveyor*. Employed surveying North and South Atlantic waters in 1991/92, Pacific & Australian waters in 1993/94.
1995 - Sold to Louis Dreyfus Armateurs S.N.C., Panama name unchanged.
1999 - Still in service as a research ship, now 1949 grt.

DE9. KABELFISKEN   116 grt   29.65 x 5.7 x 2.2
E 3-cylinder Alpha oil engine, single screw, 7.5 knots.
CT (1), **BS** (1).
1910 - Completed by W. Mulder, Stadskanaal as coaster *Drente*.
1946 - Sold & renamed *Roerdomp*.
1947 - Sold & renamed *Primo*
1972 - Converted into a cablelayer renamed *Kabelfisken*.
1999 - Owned by Arne F. Mikkelsen, Koge.

DE10. PETER FABER(3)   2854 grt   78.4 x 13.7 x 5.0
E Two 6-cylinder B & W oil engines, single screw, 2 thrusters.
CT (2), **BS** (2).
1982 - Completed by Dannebrog Verft A/S, Aarhus for Danish Government P.T.T.. Based at Korsor and strenthened for ice for duties in Greenland.
1990 - Owners became Telecom Denmark.
2000 - Still in commission.

DE11. HEIMDAL   9975 grt   135.5 x 19.4 x 6.2
E MaK 12-cylinder oil engine geared to a single screw shaft by Krupp Mak, Kiel.
CT (2), stern layer with 'A' frame and cable machinery by Hydralift of Norway.
1983 - Completed by Fredrikshavn Vaerft A/S as *Mercandian Admiral II* for K/S Merc-Skandia, Copenhagen.
1988 - Renamed *Ferrymar 1*.
1988 - Renamed *Mercandian Admiral II*.
1989 - Renamed *Heimdal* by Scandlines A/S for passenger ro-ro service between Denmark/Sweden.
6.1999 - Laid-up at Nakskov after being made redundant by new Great Belt road bridge.
9.1999 - Converted by Orskov Staalskibvaerft, Fredrikshavn into a cablelayer for Telecom Danmark International Marine. Stern rebuilt with port side funnel relocated to another part of

the vessel and the starboard funnel removed entirely. New cable tanks, cable handling machinery, underwater plough and ROV fitted, entered service in 4.2000 for worldwide fibre optics cablelaying on 3-year charter to Alcatel Submarine Networks.

DE12. MAERSK FIGHTER   3257 grt   82.5 x 18.9 x 6.2
E Two Normo 6-cylinder oil engines by Bergen Diesel A/S, twin screw,16 knots.
CT (2), **SS** (2)
9.1992 - Completed by Ulstein Verft A/S, Ulsteinvik as an oil rig supply vessel for A.P. Moller
1994 - Converted into a cablelayer, deck strengthened for heavy cargoes for Skibreder Arnold Maersk McKinney Moller, used for fibre optic cablelaying.

DE13. MAERSK DEFENDER   5746 grt   96.0 x 20.44 x 8.7
E Two MaK 8-cylinder oil engines, twin screw, 3 thrusters.
CT (2), **SS** (2)
11.1996 - Completed by Ulstein Verft A/S, Ulsteinvik for A/S D/S Svendborg (A.P. Moller).
Used for fibre optic cablelaying for both telecomms and oil-related work. A further four ships are on order to increase Maersk's share of worldwide cablelaying.

DE14. MAERSK FORWARDER 2961 grt   82.5 x 18.9 x 6.2
E Two Normo 6-cylinder oil engines by Bergen Diesel A/S, twin screw, 16 knots.
CT (2), **SS** (2)
11.1992 - Completed by Ulstein Verft A/S, Ulsteinvik for A. P. Moller.
1999 - Converted into a cablelayer at Fredericia and chartered for eight years to Global Marine Systems Ltd, Chelmsford from 1.2000.

DE15. MAERSK RECORDER   6300 grt   100.0 x 20.0 x 8.5
E 23,500 bhp diesels, twin screw, 100 tonnes bollard pull.
CT (2) with storage for 6,000 tonnes of cable. 7240 dwt.
5.2000 - Launched and 8.2000 - completed by Volkswerft, Stralsund for A. P. Moller and chartered for eight years to Global Marine Systems, Chelmsford. Stern layer capable of working in depths in excess of 3,000 metres. 60 crew. Anchor handling/towage capability. Sub-chartered for 5 years to N.T.T.W.E.M., Japan for Far-Eastern cablelayig opportunities, with plough, cable working personnel including jointers and Universal Joint equipment provided by Global Marine Systems Ltd.

DE16. MAERSK RESPONDER   6300 grt   100.0 x 20.0 x 8.5
E 23,500 bhp diesels, twin screw, 100 tonnes bollard pull.
CT (2) with storage for 6,000 tonnes of cable. 7240 dwt.
5.2000 - Launched and 9.2000 - completed by Volkswerft, Stralsund for A. P. Moller and chartered for eight years to Global Marine Systems, Chelmsford. Stern layer capable of working in depths in excess of 3,000 metres. 60 crew. Anchor handling/towage capability.

DE17. MAERSK RELIANCE   6300 grt   100.0 x 20.0 x 8.5
E 23,500 bhp diesels, twin screw, 100 tonnes bollard pull.
CT (2) with storage for 6,000 tonnes of cable. 7240 dwt.
11.2000 - Completed by Volkswerft, Stralsund for A. P. Moller and chartered for eight years to Global Marine Systems, Chelmsford. Stern layer capable of working in depths in excess of 3,000 metres. 60 crew. Anchor handling/towage capability.

DE18. MAERSK --------------   6300 grt   100.0 x 20.0 x 8.5
E   23,500 bhp diesels, twin screw, 100 tonnes bollard pull.
CT (2) with storage for 6,000 tonnes of cable. 7240 dwt.
12.2000 - Completed by Volkswerft, Stralsund for A. P. Moller and chartered for eight years to Global Marine Systems, Chelmsford. Stern layer capable of working in depths in excess of 3,000 metres. 60 crew. Anchor handling/towage capability.

NETHERLANDS.

DU1. TELEGRAAF   See *Von Podbielski* of German section GE1.

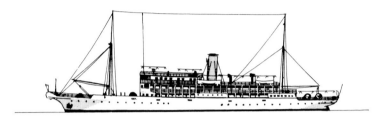

ZUIDERKRUIS

DU2. ZUIDERKRUIS   2200 grt   257.6 x 36.7 x 22.2
E   Triple expansion, twin screw, 12.5 knots.
CT (3), **BS** (2), **SS** (1).
1924 - Completed by Nederlandsche Scheepsbouw, Amsterdam for Netherlands East Indies Govt. replacing *Telegraaf*. She was also used for hydrographic surveys.
1933 - Telegraph cables gradually phased out by Netherlands. East Indies Govt. and replaced by radio.
1938 - Converted into a submarine depot ship.

DU3. POOLSTER(1)   199 grt   117.9 x 22.2 x 7.6
E   Oil engine of 200 bhp, single screw, 8.5 knots.
CT (2), **BS** (2).
1937 - Completed by Kremer & Son, Elmshorn as *Elveshorn* for Elmshorner D/S A.G., Hamburg. Chartered by Norddeutsche Seekabelwerke on a number of occasions for short lays and repair work, and engaged on cable work throughout WWII.
5.1946 - Handed over to Netherlands Govt. P.T.T. for repair of their coastal and river cables renamed *Poolster*.
6.1947 - Handed over to French Govt. P.T.T. renamed *Ingenieur en chef Hanff*, and used for the maintenance of the French domestic network of cables.
1964 - Sold for commercial trading, renamed *Le Majungais*.
1966 - Resumed coastal cablelaying for French Govt. P.T.T. under her former name.
1970 - Returned to commercial trading, renamed *Le Majungais*.
1999 - Owned by Armement Maritime Lewis, Madagascar.

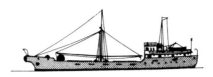

POOLSTER(2)

DU4. POOLSTER(2)   265 grt   153.6 x 23.3 x 6.9
E   Bolnes diesels, twin screw, 8 knots.
CT (1), **BS** (2)
1948 - Completed by N.V. Noord Nederlandsche Scheepswerven, Groningen for Neth. Govt.
P.T.T. and used for repair of river and coastal cables.
1970 - Sold to commercial fishing interests renamed *Zeester,* subsequently broken up.

DIRECTEUR - GENERAAL BAST

DU5. DIRECTEUR-GENERAAL BAST   500 grt   180.1 x 30.9 x 10.6
E   5-cylinder Bolnes diesels 700 bhp, twin screw, 10.6 knots.
CT (2), **BS** (2).
5.1969 - Completed by E.J. Smit, Westerbroek for Staatsbed. der Post Telegraphique &
Telefonie. Used for repair of coastal and river cables.
1989 - Sold & renamed *VSO Surveyor 1*
1991 - Sold to Seateam Subsea Support B.V., Den Helder renamed *STM Vega.*

DU6. FLEXSERVICE 1   6805 grt   425.6 x 57.5 x 22.4
E Doxford oil engine of 2600 bhp, single screw, 11.5 knots. 4 thrusters.
1960 - Completed as the ore carrier *Ravensworth* of 9740 dwt by Austin & Pickersgill Ltd,
Sunderland for her Newcastle trampship owners R. S. Dalgleish Ltd.
1975 - Purchased by Flex Service N.V. for conversion into a flexible pipelayer. She was
converted by Kristiansand Mek Verksted by the insertion of four large cable reels, three in the
holds and one on deck. Flexible pipe was loaded under tension onto the reels, and laid under
tension over her twin bow sheaves while she moved astern. Dynamic-positioning systems.
1976 - Renamed *Flexservice 1* carried out her first contract in the Brent field in August,1976,
laying flexible pipes and power cables.
1995 - Sold to Panamanian owners, name unchanged. Now fitted with three vertical cylinder
baskets for holding flexible pipe.

The electricity cable made fast below an inflatable tube is lowered over the stern of the ship and towed ashore, then winched up the beach and slipway into place in St Peter Port

Tony Rive

During the summer a most unusual looking ship was seen working in the Channel Islands. She was the *Sea Spider*, 4,008 gt, a cable-laying vessel built in 1999 owned by Van der Stoel Shipping of the Netherlands. She was laying fibre optic cables and a new electricity cable between Guernsey, Jersey and France.

Her giant "turntable" can hold 4,000 tonnes of cable and she is capable of laying cables extremely accurately, both in depth and position, using all the most modern devices available. These include underwater survey cameras and a robot submarine.

The "Fort George" (A388) at Gosport, January 10 1994

A. Blackler

RFA Ship Re-named ● Cable Lavin...

Islands ● Their I

came about because there has been some confusion with another RFA ship, the **Fort George**, 28,821 gt. **Fort Rosalie** is an historic name – it is a fort in Canada – and there has been a previous **Rosalie** in the fleet.

Ship Named After Company Father

The latest ship to join the A P Møller (Maersk Line) fleet was named in early June. She is the **A P Møller** and was named after the founder of the company, Arnold Peter Møller. He founded the company in 1951. The ship is the latest "S" class container ship and has a capacity of about 6,600 TEU. She was built for the ...se Steel

1995 - Sold to Panamanian owners, name unchanged. Now fitted with three vertical cylinder baskets for holding flexible pipe.
2000 - Still in commission.

DU7. FLEXSERVICE 2   2652 grt   81.3 x 18.4 x 4.3
E Two 12-cylinder Polar oil engines, 2 controllable pitch propellers, 4 thrusters.
CT (2), **SS** (2)
1979 - Completed by Ankerlokken Verft Floro A/S, Floro for Flex Service N.V., an ORSV type with accurate dynamic positioning systems and considerable pipelaying ability to stream up to four lines of flexible oil pipes over her wide stern.
1986 - Sold to Johannes Ostensjo, Haugesund renamed *Edda Sea*.
1987 - Sold to Sandfrak Rederi A/S, Haugesund renamed *Nor Truck*.
1988 - Sold to Sea Truck (UK) Ltd, Aberdeen renamed *Sea Truck*.

DU8. FLEXSERVICE 3   5662 grt   107.1 x 19.4 x 8.4
E Two Wartsila oil engines of 3710 bhp, two controllable pitch propellers, 3 thrusters.
CT (3) of total capacity 1,500 cu.m. or 3200 tonnes, also spare tank. Two linear cable engines, two drum engines of 4m diameter. **SS** (2).
1982 - Completed by Marstrandverken, Marstrand for Flex Service N.V. for oil-related work.
1992 - Converted to a cableship, lengthened to the above dimensions.
1995 - Sold to SB Submarine Systems Ltd (Cable & Wireless(Marine), Nassau),managers, and laid first China/Korea system.
1998 - Renamed *Fu Lai* for long-term contract to China Telecom. Based at Shanghai and provides services to Yokohama Cable Maintenance Agreement, and has also laid segments of FLAG, SEA-ME-WE3 and China/U.S.A. systems.

DU9. FRESNEL   6475 grt   103.5 x 23.2 x 7.05
E Three Normo 9-cylinder oil engines, twin screw, 15.5 knots. 4 thrusters:
CT (3), **SS** (2).
1997 - Completed by Ulstein Verft A/S, Ulstein for Care Offshore Netherlands B.V. with SOSEMA of Dunkirk as managers for oil-related flexible pipelaying/cablelaying work in the North Sea oilfields.

DU10. DOCK EXPRESS 20   14413 grt   169.6 x 25.7 x 6.75
E Two Werkspoor 6-cylinder oil engines, 2 controllable pitch propellers, 3 thrusters.
1983 - Completed by Verolme Scheeps. Heusden B.V. for Dockwise 20 N.V., Willemstad as a heavy load vessel/ro-ro ship with stern docking facilities.
1989 - Converted to cablelayer for same owners. Loads cable to a mean draft of 6.75 metres. Worldwide activities, including loading of American-manufactured cable and equipment at Portsmouth, New Hampshire factory of Tyco. On charter to Tyco Submarine Systems Ltd (TSSL) as a stern layer from modified stern, but retains her two heavy-lift gantries. Dockwise have ordered an optic fibre cablelayer from Hyundai Mipo Dockyard, Korea for delivery in 2001, with an option for another.

DU11. SEA SPIDER   5500 dwt   86.1 x 24.0 x 4.5
E Cummins-Wartsila diesel-electric power plant. 10 knots. 51 crew.
1 Deck Cable Carousel with capacity for holding 4,800 tons of power or optic fibre cable. Cable machinery on aft of main deck comprises three cable engines, one trencher with umbilical winch and an 'A' - frame of 50 tonnes capacity.

4.1999 - Completed by Scheepswerf De Hoop, Lobith, Netherlands for Van der Stoel Cable, Netherlands to lay power cables between Sweden and Poland. Completed in 9 months for tight deadline contract with Swedish power company SwePol Link A/B and Polish power company PPGC. Cables manufactured by High Voltage Cables A/B, Karlskrona with two full loads of cable taken from Karlskrona in May,1999. The complete power system was handed over in January,2000, and *Sea Spider* undertook her next contract in the Channel Islands in the summer of 2000.

NORWAY.

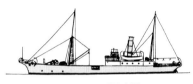

TELEGRAF

NO1. TELEGRAF   227 grt   135.0 x 20.3 x 10.3
E   Compound, single screw, 8.5 knots.
CT (1), **BS** (2).
1894 - Completed by Kristiansand Mek. Verks. for Norwegian Govt. P.T.T. and based at Bergen for the maintenance of coastal cables.
1957 - Sold out of the cable world renamed Tryggheim.
26.10.1967 - Sank at Gildeshal, subsequently raised and towed to Bodo for examination, and then scrapped.

NO2. LANDEGO   344 grt   128.0 x 24.1 x 12.3
E   Triple expansion, single screw, 10 knots.
CT (1) **BS** (2).
1927 - Completed by Moss Verft A/S, Moss for the Norwegian Govt. P.T.T.
1942 - Mined/sunk to North of Harstad.

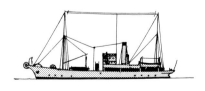

LANDEGO

NO3. NORDKABEL   85 grt   72.0 x 20.5
& NO4. SORKABEL
E Diesel.
CT (1), **BS** (1).
1947/48 - Both completed at Drammen. *Sorkabel* based at Bergen, *Nordkabel* based at Bodo
and in 1970 converted into a transport workshop for the P.T.T. and renamed *Tele 5* and based
at Bergen. Existence of both in doubt at millennium.

TELEKABEL

NO5. TELEKABEL   860 grt   185.9 x 32.9 x 13.9
E Diesel, 1260 bhp. 13 knots.
CT (2), **BS** (2).
1957 - Completed by Glommens Mek Verksted, Fredrikstad for Norwegian Govt. P.T.T. and
based at Bergen for maintenace of coastal cables.
1995 - Sold to Numenor International Inc, Panama renamed *Vulcain*.

NO6. NORDKABEL(2)   230 grt   111.2 x 26.4 x 10.4
E Diesel, 600 bhp. 11 knots.
CT (1), **BS** (1).
1969 - Completed by G. Eides Sonner A/S, Hoylandsbydd for Norwegian Govt. P.T.T. and
based at Bodo for maintenance of Northern coastal cables.
1989 - Lengthened to 44.1 metres.
1999 - Owned by Bulk Transport A/S, Bodo - still in use as a cablelayer.

NO7. ELEKTRON   1628 grt   253.9 x 46.0 x 9.9
E 8-cylinder Atlas-MaK oil engine of 1500 bhp.
CT (2), **BS** (2).
1969 - Completed by Trondheim M.V. for Norwegian Water Resources & Electricity Board
to carry out feasibility studies for the Skagerrak power cables.
1999 - Owned by Statnett Rederi A/S, Oslo.

NO8. SKAGERRAK   7172 grt   278.9 x 108.3 x 19.7
E Three Normo 12-cylinder Vee oil engines by A/S Bergens M/V, Bergen.
1976 - Completed by Ogrey M.V., Kristiansand for Norwegian Water Resources & Electricity
Board to lay power cables across the Skagerrak between Kristiansand and Lild Strand,
Denmark. She is in essence a wide barge usually towed around to locations, with her engines
used only for manoeuvrability when laying cables.
1977 - Laid second Skagerrak power cables
1999 - Owned by Statnett Rederi A/S, Oslo.

6.2000 - Purchased by Havila Supply A/S, Norway for $14.3M for charter to Alcatel Kabel Norge up to 2004. Initial cable burial charter to Alcatel in the North Sea was completed during 8.2000.

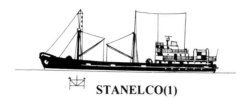

STANELCO(1)

NO9. STANELCO(1)   319 grt   156.6 x 22.1 x 9.2
E Oil engines, twin screw.
CT (1), **BS** (2) replaced by large skid.
1944 - Completed by Teesside Bridge & Eng. Works as a landing craft.
1946 - Purchased by Standard Telefon og Kabelfabrik and converted for laying power cables in Norwegian coastal waters. Replaced by *Stanelco* (2).

NO10. STANELCO(2)   1692 grt   64.22 x 13.3 x 4.7
E 9-cylinder Normo oil engine by A/S Bergens M/V, single screw, 12 knots.
CT (1), **BS** (2).
1975 - Completed by Brattvag Skips., Brattvag as coaster *Siraholm*.
1982 - Converted into a cablelayer, renamed *Stanelco* (2).
2000 - Now owned by Alcatel Contracting Norway A/S, Oslo.

NO11. KYSTKABEL   331 grt   26.8 x 5.7 x 2.2
E Two General Motors 12-cylinder diesels of 1080 bhp, twin screw.
CT (1), **BS** (2).
1985 - Completed as a cablelayer by Tronderverftet A/S, Hommelvik.
2000 - Now owned by Alcatel Contracting Norway A/S, Namsos.

NO12. VIKING LADY   4160 grt   105.4 x 22.0 x 8.6
E Two 12-cyl Wichmann diesels, 2 controllable pitch propellers, 4 thrusters.
CT (2) 5,000 tonne cable capacity, **SS** (2).
1996 - Completed by Flekkefjord Slipp & Mask A/S, Norway for K/S Eidesvik & Co A/S, Haugesund as an oil rig supply vessel/survey ship/supply ship. Eidesvik have carried out many route surveys in the past, a recent survey of 15,000 km of the seabed around South America from the Virgin Islands via the Magellan Strait to Peru and the Panama Canal was carried out for Alcatel Submarine Networks, and other work has been done in the Mediterranean.
7.2000 - Conversion to cablelayer completed by Astilleros de Cadiz for a 5-year charter to Caldwell Cable Ventures, a subsidiary of General Dynamics of the U.S.A. Lengthened by 13 metre mid-section, and larger power generators installed.

The Bergen-registered research/cable layer Oceanic King, 12,867grt, of Polar Ship Management; she was completed by Flekkefjord Slip. & Maas. AS, Flekkefjord, in 2000 as the Polar King, being renamed in 2000.

Pictures: Mike Prendergast, North Ryde.

3/02

The container ship Bunga Mas Satu, 7,998grt, of the Malaysian International Shipping Corp., Malaysia; she was completed by SA Juliana Construction Gijonese, Gijon, in 1995.

The Antigua & Barbuda-registered container ship Ankara, 9,616grt, built by Stoczia Szczecinska, Szczecin, in 1996 for the Northern Ocean Shipping Co.

NO13. POLAR -----   4000 grt   90.0 x 18.0 x 6.0
E Two oil engines geared to two controllable pitch propellers, 4 thrusters.
4,000 tonne cable capacity.
2001 - Due for completion in Norway for Polar Ship Management A/S, Bergen as a dual-purpose Arctic/Antarctic support ship/cablelayer. Helicopter platform aft. Starboard crane of 10-tonne capacity. Crew and research scientists/cablelaying personnel will number well over 100. Polar Ship Management A/S already operate two hydrographic research vessels in their fleet, *Polar Queen* completed by Kvaerner at Leirvik in 1995 and *Polar King* completed by Flekkefjord A/S during 2000.

NO14. SKANDI -------   4000 grt
E Two oil engines geared to two controllable pitch propellers, 4 thrusters.
5,000 tonne cable capacity.
4,2001 - Due for completion by Aker Brattvaag Skipsverft A/S, Brattvaag as a supply vessel/cablelayer for District Offshore A/S, Bergen. She will begin a 6-year time charter to CTC Marine Projects for deployment with Alcatel Submarine Systems. The vessel's hull was finished during 8.2000 by Santierul Naval Tulcea shipyard, Romania and then towed to Norway for completion during 9.2000. District Offshore A/S have a large fleet of standby safety vessels; anchor-handling, fire-fighting tugs; oil rig supply vessels; and offshore well-stimulation vessels.

REST OF THE WORLD

BAHAMAS

BA1. JASMINE PROTECTOR   1558 grt   55.4 x 24.0 x 2.7
E   Four Deutz 6-cylinder oil engines, quad screw. 6.5 knots.
1966 - Completed by Kieler Howaldtswerke A.G., Kiel as sheerlegs pontoon *Magnus III*.
1987 - Converted to workship TAK 300-93.
1993 - Sold to Nassau owners & renamed *Jasmine*.
1994 - Converted to cablelayer/repairer and renamed *Jasmine Protector*.
2000 - Still in commission.

BARBADOS

BB1. AGILE   9402 grt   139.4 x 20.25 x 6.2
E   Two 6-cylinder Pielstick oil engines geared to two screw shafts, thrusters, 14 knots.
CT (5), **SS** (2)
1978 - Completed by Hollming O/Y, Rauma as heavy-lift/barge carrier *Stakhanovets Kotov* for Russian Navy.
1996 - Sold and renamed *Len Speer*.
1998 - Sold to Secunda Global Marine, Nova Scotia and converted in Canada to a stern cablelayer renamed *Agile*, for 5-year charter to Cable & Wireless Global Marine.
1999 - AmericasII system cablelaying from U.S./ Caribbean/South America.
6.1999 - Transfer to Global Marine Systems Ltd.
2000 - PAC1 system cablelaying from Panama to Southern California based at San Diego.

BB2. BOLD ENDURANCE   9802 grt   139.4 x 20.25 x 6.2
E   Two 6-cylinder Pielstick oil engines geared to two screw shafts, thrusters, 14 knots.
CT (5), **SS** (2)
1978 - Completed by Hollming O/Y, Rauma as heavy-lift/barge carrier *Stakhanovets Petrash* for Russian Navy.
1997 - Sold to Dove Navigation Ltd renamed *Fastov*.
1999 - Sold to Secunda Global Marine, Nova Scotia and converted by Hyundai H.I., South Korea into a stern cablelayer, and renamed *Bold Endurance* for 5-year charter to Global Marine Systems Ltd, Chelmsford. Cable handling gear installed on Teesside.
2.2000 - Conversion completed and began sub-charter to KDD Submarine Systems for Far Eastern project. She was briefly named *Astana*.

BELGIUM

BE1. DISCOVERY   8248 grt   120.47 x 19.73 x 6.5
E   Four Wartsila 6-cyl oil engines driving 4 generators connected to 3 electric motors, triple screw. 12 knots.
CT (3), **BS** (2). Coiling capacity of 1497 cu. metres.
1990 - Completed by N.V. Boelwerf S.A., Temse for N.V. Friary Ocean Surveyor, Luxembourg as a cableship/diving support ship for oil-related work.

DISCOVERY under repair in the Tyne (Author)

CANADA

CA1. NEWFIELD   785 grt   206.4 x 29.1 x 16.8

E Compound, single screw.

CT (1), **BS** (2)

9.1870 - Completed by Robert Thompson, Sunderland for Wilkinson & Co.,Hartlepool.

1880 - Purchased by Canadian Govt. and fitted out for cable work for repair of short cables connecting islands in the St. Lawrence and Nova Scotia areas with the mainland e.g. Anticosti Island and Magdalen Island.

22.9.1900 - Aground and wrecked near Digby (NS).

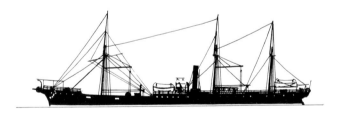

TYRIAN

CA2. TYRIAN   1039 grt   237.5 x 30.2 x 19.9

E Compound, single screw.

CT (2), **BS** (2), **SS** (1)

1869 - Completed by Robert Duncan & Co., Port Glasgow for Mediterranean services of Anchor Line.

1870/76 - Served Glasgow/Halifax(NS) and Glasgow/St. John(NB).

1888/92 - Served New York/Jamaica.

1.1893 - Sold to Archibald Colvil, New York for same Jamaican service.

1902 - Sold to Canadian Govt. and converted into a cablelayer. She and the new *Lady Laurier* maintained the St. Lawrence cables and replaced *Newfield*.

1935 - Broken up after 33 years cable service for Canadian Govt.

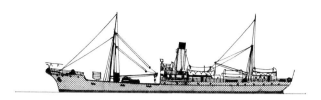

LADY LAURIER

CA3. LADY LAURIER   1051 grt   214.9 x 34.2 x 17.7
E Triple expansion, twin screw, 14 knots.
CT (2), **BS** (2), **SS** (1).
1902 - Completed by Fleming & Ferguson, Paisley as a cableship for Canadian Govt. to replace *Newfield*. Based at Halifax(NS). Duplicated Gaspe/Anticosti Island and Cape Breton Island/Magdalen Island cables.
1959 - Broken up after 57 years of cable repair work, some of her artefacts are in the Maritime Museum in Halifax(NS).

CA4. PRINCESS LOUISE 932 grt   180.0 x 30.0 x 13.0
E Paddle, 10 knots.
CT (1) with a vertical donkey boiler on deck providing the steam for the cable machinery.
1869 - Completed by J. Inglis, New York as *Olympia* for Oregon Steam Navigation Company for New York/Seattle & Victoria service via Cape Horn.
1878 - Sold to Hudson's Bay Company and renamed *Princess Louise*.
1883 - Transferred to Canadian Pacific Navigation Company, Victoria/Vancouver.
1901 - Transferred to Canadian Pacific Railways, Victoria/Vancouver.
1906 - Sold to a Victoria owner and converted into a dredging barge two years later.
1913 - Laid Victoria/Vancouver loaded telephone cable, the longest telephone cable in service for many years with the cable stored in her holds.
1919 - Sank at Port Alice(BC).

CA5. BLUETHROAT   560 grt   157.0 x 33.0 x 14.6
E Diesel engine of 1200 bhp, twin screw, 12 knots.
CT (1), **BS** (2)
1955 - Completed by George T. Dare & Son Ltd, Lauzon for Canadian Govt. as a controlled minelayer but also capable of cablelaying for harbour defence work. Previously, the Flower class corvette *Sackville* and two trawler types, *Whitethroat* and *Stonechat*, had been transferred from the Royal Navy for these duties in 1944.

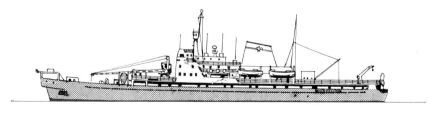

JOHN CABOT

CA6. JOHN CABOT   5097 grt   313.3 x 60.3 x 34.2
E Diesel-electric, twin screw, 12 knots.
CT (3), **BS** (3), **SS** (1).
15.4.1964 - Launched and 6.1965 completed by Canadian Vickers, Montreal for Canadian Govt. as a combined ice-breaker/cableship operated by the Canadian Coastguard for Canadian Overseas Telecommunications Corp. Her four diesel-generators were given enough power for icebreaking and she was fitted with forward and aft thrusters and heeling tanks to help free her when stuck in heavy ice. Helicopter, 100 crew.
1973 - Used for ploughing work on Canadian shore ends of CANTAT2 Transatlantic coaxial.
10.1974 - Suffered serious fire.
1976 - Owners renamed Teleglobe.
1994 - Sold to Teleglobe Consulting Co. Ltd, Montreal (Cable & Wireless,mgrs).
1996 - Sold to McDermott Subsea Services and arrived in the Tees during 9.1996 for modernisation for a new role as a cableship.
1997 - Sold on completion of work to Elettra spA, Naples and renamed *Certamen* for cable work in the Mediterranean with Italcable. Loads cable at the Pirelli pier at Arco Felice, Pozzuoli near Naples.

CHINA

CH1. FEE CHEU   1034 grt   220.0 x 32.1 x 20.0
Single screw, triple expansion engine 1000 ihp, 13 knots.
1887 - Completed by William Doxford & Sons Ltd, Sunderland for J. Liu, Formosa.
1896 - Purchased by Chinese Govt. and fitted out for cable work for coastal work from Canton to Shanghai to Tientsin. Out of commission after WWI.

CH2. FU LAI   See *Flexservice 3* in Dutch section

EMIRATES

EM1. ETISALAT   2221 grt   74.25 x 13.22 x 4.54
E Two Wartsila 6-cylinder oil engines of 2650 bhp, controllable pitch propeller.
CT (2), **BS** (2), **SS** (1).
11.1990 - Completed as a cableship by Masa Yards Inc, Helsinki for Emirates Telecomms Corporation, Abu Dhabi. Bow sheaves. Two decks, one of these containing the cablelaying control machinery and cable testing areas and extending to the bow. Accomodation block extends from 'midships to the stern where a large 'A' frame is situated, aft of her twin funnels

EM2. UMM-AL-ANBER   7750 grt   108.64 x 20.45 x 5.8
E Two 8-cylinder oil engines by Lindholmen A/B, Gothenburg, 2 controllable pitch propellers, forward thruster. 18 knots.
CT (2), **BS** (2), **SS** (1)
1972 - Completed by Ankerloken Verft as ro-ro *Ilkka* of 1566 grt.
1979 - Sold to Javelin Shipping Co. Ltd & renamed *Lagan Bridge*
1980 - Renamed *Lady Tone*
1983 - Sold to Merchant Ferries,London, renamed *Merchant Navigator*.

1990 - Converted to research/diving support ship *Geomaster*.
1996 - Converted to cableship *Umm-al-Anber* for Emirates Telecommunications Corp., Abu Dhabi. Operates as both cablelayer and repairer.

ESTONIA

ES1. KOMPASS   415 grt
1918 - Completed and in commission as a cableship for Estonian Govt. until 1938 for coastal, naval and harbour defence work. The international telegraph connections from Estonia were handled by the Great Northern Telegraph Company of Denmark.

FINLAND

FN1. TELEPAATTI   322 grt   36.6 x 7.7 x 2.6
E   6-cylinder Wartsila oil engine of 1000 bhp, single screw. 10 knots.
CT (1), **BS** (1), **SS** (1)
1978 - Completed by Rauma-Repola O/Y, Savonlinna for Finnish Govt. P.T.T. Dept., Turku, Western Finland. Ice-strengthened, machinery aft, 2 side thrusters.

GREECE

THALIS O. MILISSIOS at Glyfada   (Author)

The wooden bridge and forward fixed cable drum of THALIS O. MILISSIOS (Author)

GR1. THALIS O MILISSIOS   842 grt   142.0 x 32.0 x 21.8
E Compound engines by builder, twin screw.
CT (1), **BS** (2), cable drum located on fo'c'stle, which was connected by cat walk to wooden bridge on starboard side only, cable machinery, buoys & grapnels in well deck. Two decks of accomodation, upper of teak.
1909 - Completed as *Joseph Henry* (q.v.) by Newport News SB & DD Co. for U.S. Army.
1939 - The only cablelayer owned by U.S. Government.
1947 - Transferred to Greek Govt. for maintenance of coastal cables.
1968 - Over one hundred cables in Greek waters maintained by Greek Government, only three owned by Cable & Wireless Ltd.
1991 - Laid-up at Glyfada marina as a museum ship. Her cable hold contains photographs and an exhibition, and she still retains most of her cableship features.

GR2. THALIS   See *Peter Faber*(2) in Danish Section.

GR3. KERAVNOS   322 grt   33.2 x 12.0 x 2.2
E Two MWM 12-cylinder oil engines of 756 bhp, twin screw, machinery aft.
CT (1), **BS** (1),
1973 - Completed by G. Koronaios Bros. Ltd, Perama as cableship for Fulship Maritime Co., Piraeus.
1999 - Still in commission.

GR4. SUB ONE   325 grt   49.7 x 8.3 x 3.5
E 6-cylinder Alpha diesel of 600 bhp, single screw. 11 knots.
CT (1), **BS** (1)
1975 - Completed by A/S Nordsovaerftet, Ringkobing as coaster *Hans Boye*, Danish owner.
1985 - Converted to a cableship renamed *Batelco One*.
1994 - Sold to Piraeus owners & renamed *Sub One*.
1999 - Still in commission.

INDIA

AMBERWITCH

IN1. AMBERWITCH   441 grt   175.0 x 27.0 x 16.5
E Compound, single screw.
CT (2), **BS** (2), **SS** (1)
1862 - Completed by James Laing & Co., Sunderland as *Charente*.

1864 - Purchased by Indian Govt. and fitted out as a cable repair ship for the Persian Gulf cables linking Gwadar, now part of Pakistan, to Bushire and Fao near the Shatt-el-Arab to link with Turkish landlines. A duplicate was laid in 1869 as traffic including British Army messages was heavy. The 1870 Eastern Group cable from Suez/Aden/Bombay laid by *Great Eastern* took much of this traffic, but maintenance of the Persian Gulf cables was kept up by *Amberwitch* until 1879 when the new *Patrick Stewart*(1) arrived.

PATRICK STEWART(1)

IN2. PATRICK STEWART(1)   1130 grt   226.0 x 30.75 x 16.5
E Compound, single screw.
CT (4), **BS** (2), **SS** (1), cable machinery in forward well deck.
1879 - Completed by J. Key & Sons, Kirkcaldy for Indian Govt. and named after first Director General of India Telegraphs.
1901 - Laid Jask/Muscat cable manufactured by Siemens Bros.
1924 - Sold after a career of 45 years repairing the Persian Gulf and Indian Ocean cables based at Karachi.

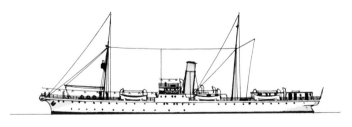

PATRICK STEWART(2)

IN3. PATRICK STEWART(2)   1572 grt   248.0 x 37.5 x 13.3
E Triple expansion, twin screw.
CT (3), **BS** (2). Clarke,Chapman & Co. Ltd of Gateshead supplied two cable machines each with their own steam-driven engines and installed on port and starboard sides of main deck forward.
1924 - Completed by William Simons Ltd, Renfrew for Indian Govt. to a design by Sir J.H. Biles & Co. and arrived at Karachi during 8.1925 as a repair ship for the Persian Gulf and Indian Ocean cables. Accomodation for 13 passengers was also included.
1930 - Sold to Eastern Telegraph Company, name unchanged.

1932 - Sold to Royal Indian Navy and converted into a survey ship renamed *Investigator*.
1951 - Out of service.

INDONESIA.
ID1. BIDUK   1250 displacement   273.2 x 39.5 x 16.5
E   Triple expansion, single screw.
1952 - Completed by J. & K. Smit, Kinderdijk for Indonesian Govt. as a combined cableship, lighthouse tender and naval auxiliary.
2000 - Existence in doubt.

ITALY.

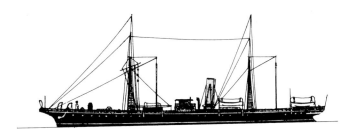

CITTA di MILANO(1)

IT1. CITTA di MILANO(1) 1247 grt   240.0 x 33.2 x 16.9
E   Compound, single screw, 11 knots.
CT (2), **BS** (2), **SS** (1)
1886 - Completed by Robert Thompson & Sons, Sunderland for the Pirelli Company with cable factories in both Milan and Spezia.
6.1887 - Entered service of Italian Military Marine for laying of Pirelli cables to Sicily and the Lipari Islands.
16.6.1919 - Foundered off Eolie Islands after striking a reef while repairing a telegraph cable, 26 lost out of crew of 85.

IT2. CITTA di MILANO(2)   See *Grossherzog von Oldenburg* in German section.

IT3. GIASONE(1)   1558 tons displacement   247.2 x 33.7 x 12.7
E   Triple expansion, twin screw, 16 knots. 90 crew.
CT (2), **BS** (2), **SS** (2).
1929 - Completed by Breda Company at their Marghera(Venice) yard for Italian Govt. as a combined cableship/boom defence/salvage ship/auxiliary for use by Italian Navy.
4.10.1940 - Mined/sunk on a voyage from Trapani to Pantellaria.

IT4. GIASONE(2)   1715 tons displacement   251.3 x 33.1 x 12.9
E   Triple expansion, twin screw. 15 knots.
CT (2), **BS** (2), **SS** (2)
1941 - Completed by Ansaldo Co., Genoa for Italian Navy as an almost identical replacement for the lost ship of the same name.
1943 - Captured by Germans at Genoa.
1945 - Found sunk in Marseilles at end of the war, refloated and taken over by French Govt. renamed *D'Arsonval* (q.v.).

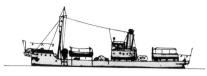

RAMPINO

IT5. RAMPINO 654 tons displacement 154.3 x 24.2 x 11.8
E Triple expansion, single screw, 9 knots.
CT (1), **BS** (2)
1922 - Completed by Harburg-Holts, Hamburg as a trawler.
1.1942 - Purchased by Italian Navy and converted at Giudecca yard, Venice into a cableship, commissioned on 19.4.1943.
1953 - Converted into a lighthouse tender and still in commission in 1978.

ITM VENTURER, seen on the Tees, is now the Italian cableship GIULIO VERNE (Author)

IT6. SALERNUM See *Charles Brown* in American section.
IT7. GIULIO VERNE See *ITM Venturer* of British section.
IT8. CERTAMEN See *John Cabot* in Canadian section.

IT9. TELIRI 8345 grt 111.5 x 19.0 x 12.5
E Diesel-electric, 3 Wartsila oil engines driving 3 generators connected to 2 electric motors. Twin screw. 3750 bhp 16.5 knots.
CT (3), **SS** (2)
1996 - Completed by Fincantieri Cant. Nav. Italiani spA, Livorno for Euroshipping spA di Nav., Catania for charter to Italcable. Suitable for either optical fibre cablelaying or oil-related work, with one 23-tonne crane and two 10-tonne cranes on clear aft work deck.

KOREA.

KO1. SEGERO   8323 grt   115.4 x 20.0 x 7.8
E   Diesel-electric, 4 Alpha oil engines driving generators connected to 2 electric motors and reduction geared to twin shafts. 15 knots.
CT (3), **BS** (2), **SS** (1)
4.1998 - Completed by Hanjin Heavy Industries Co. Ltd, Pusan for KT Shipping S.A.,Panama for charter to Korea Submarine Telecomms Ltd. Ice-strengthened cable-layer/repairer. Bow sheaves, two decks with one carrying cablelaying machinery and cable testing areas.

LIBERIA.

LI1. SEAWAY EAGLE   9556 grt   142.4 x 19.94 x 5.5
E   Diesel-electric. Four Wartsila 6-cylinder oil engines driving four generators connected to three electric motors, triple screw. 13 knots.
1994 - Launched as *Navigator* by Boelwerf N.V., Temse for N.V. Friary Ocean Surveyor, Belgium.
4.1997 - Completed as *Seaway Eagle* for SCS Shipping Ltd (Stolt Comex Seaway A/S) by Koninklijke Scheldegroep B.V., Vlissingen as a cableship/supply ship.

NEW ZEALAND.

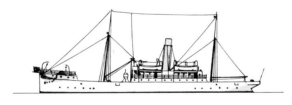

TUTANEKAI

NZ1. TUTANEKAI   811 grt   205.6 x 30.1 x 14.8
E   Triple expansion, twin screw.
CT (1), **BS** (2).
1896 - Completed by D. J. Dunlop & Co., Port Glasgow for New Zealand Govt. as a combined cableship/yacht/minesweeper/lighthouse tender.
1900 - Tour of Pacific islands with a Govt. party.
1920 - Became the South Island/Stewart Island ferry.
1930 - Broken up.

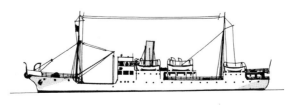

MATAI

NZ2. MATAI 1050 grt   219.0 x 30.1 x 14.8

E   Triple expansion, twin screw.

CT (1), **BS** (2)

1930 - Completed by Hawthorn, Leslie & Co. Ltd, Hebburn for New Zealand Govt. as a combined cableship/lighthouse tender/minesweeper with more emphasis on cable work than *Tutanekai*.

1940/45 - Used for harbour defence cable work by R.N.Z.N.

1950 - Bass Strait telephone cable repair   (Australian Govt.)

10.1959 - Became the Stewart Island ferry.

1963 - Sold to Hong Kong Shipping Co, Panama renamed *Zetai Star*.

1970 - Broken up.

PANAMA.

PA1. SUNRISE 2000   10648 grt   123.0 x 30.0 x 7.0

Two 6-cylinder Hanshin oil engines sr geared to two screws.

1984 - Completed by Kanasashi Co. Ltd, Toyohashi as a heavy load ship *Sunrise*.

1994 - Purchased by Sunflex Offshore N.V.(Coflexip Stena Offshore Ltd) and converted to a flexible flowlinelayer, renamed *Sunrise 2000*.

7/1999 - Recommissioned by Coflexip Stena Offshore as a deepwater flexible flowlinelayer after a 45 day refit at the Rio de Janeiro Navy Dockyard to enable her to undertake operations in deeper waters to a depth of 2,000 metres. She has a large bridge situated over her fo'c'stle, wide hull to handle large cable drums and other heavy equipment, and is a stern layer.

PHILIPPINES.

PH1. J. BUSTAMENTE   1074 grt   221.9 x 33.0 x 15.7

E   Triple expansion, single screw.

CT (2), **BS** (3).

1904 - Completed by Cia Trasatlantica, Cadiz for commercial trading by Cia General de Tabacos de Filipinos, Manila.

1922 - Purchased by Philippine Govt. and fitted out for cable work at Havana by the Marine Repair yard of the Bureau of Commerce & Trading.

1936 - Renamed *Apo* by the Philippine Government.

WWII Loss.

POLAND.

PO1. KABLOWEIC   1050 displacement

1956 - Commissioned by Polish Govt. for maintenance of coastal cables and harbour defence systems. The Great Northern Telegraph Company of Denmark maintained the international connections to Poland until the 1980s.

SINGAPORE

SG1. ASEAN RESTORER   11156 grt   131.4 x 21.8 x 6.5
E Diesel-electric propulsion comprising 5 Wartsila Vasa oil engines(three of 9-cylinder & two of 6-cylinder) connected to 5 electric generators. 16 knots. 4 thrusters.
CT (3) of total capacity 4500 cu. metres or 7,000 tonnes of cable with a fourth tank designed to carry spares with an inner ring separating up to 300 cu. metres of cable. Two linear cable engines; starboard of 16 tonne capacity & port of 12 tonnes at 1.5 knots cable recovery speed.
SS (2) of 4 metres diameter over which an 'A' frame is fitted.
9.1994 - Completed by Kvaerner Masa Yards, Turku for International Cableship Pte Ltd, Singapore. 64 crew + 17 berths for cable technicians and observers. Bare-boat charter to Asean Cableship Company for SEAIOCMA (South East Asia, Indian Ocean Cable Maintenance Agreement). Sister of *Cable Retriever*.

SG2. CABLE RETRIEVER   11156 grt   131.4 x 21.8 x 6.5
E Diesel-electric propulsion comprising 5 Wartsila Vasa oil engines(three of 9-cylinder & two of 6-cylinder) connected to 5 electric generators. 16 knots. 4 thrusters.
CT (3) of total capacity 4500 cu. metres or 7,000 tonnes of cable with a fourth tank designed to carry spares with an inner ring separating up to 300 cu. metres of cable. Two linear cable engines; starboard of 16 tonne capacity & port of 12 tonnes at 1.5 knots cable recovery speed.
SS (2) of 4 metres diameter over which an 'A' frame is fitted.
10.1997 - Completed by Kvaerner Masa Yards, Turku for International Cableship Pte Ltd, Singapore. 64 crew + 17 berths for cable technicians and observers. Bare-boat charter to Asean Cableship Company for SEAIOCMA (South East Asia, Indian Ocean Cable Maintenance Agreement). Sister of *Asean Restorer*.

SOUTH AFRICA

SA1. CABLE RESTORER See *Bullfrog* of Royal Navy section

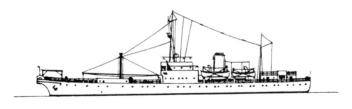

CABLE RESTORER

SPAIN

CASTILLO OLMEDO

SP1. CASTILLO OLMEDO   1481 grt   268.4 x 35.9 x 18.3

E   Triple expansion, single screw.

CT (2), **BS** (2), **SS** (1).

1908 - Completed by Nylands Verksted, Oslo for Akties Vestheim (H. Ditlev-Simonsen & Co, Oslo) for commercial trading as *Juan*.

1934 - Sold to A/S D/S Bjornoy (Olav B. Hess), Bergen renamed *Bjornoy*.

1937 - Sold to Spanish owners renamed *Reina*

1937/38 - Sunk during Spanish Civil War but salvaged, refitted & renamed *Castillo Olmedo* in 1939.

1944/46 - Converted into a cableship for Spanish Government.

1969 - Broken up.

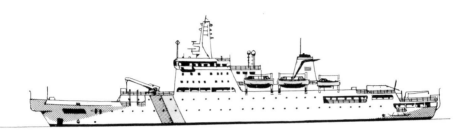

ATLANTIDA

SP2. ATLANTIDA   7374 grt   114.03 x 18.55 x 6.0

E   Three 8-cylinder Sulzer oil engines driving 3 generators connected to four electric motors. Twin screw. 15.8 knots. Two thrusters.

CT (3), **BS** (2), **SS** (1), cable machinery in enclosed main cable deck.

1988 - Completed by Astilleros de Santander S.A., Santander for Telecommunicaciones Marinas S.A., Santa Cruz de Tenerife. Twin-funnelled, ice-strengthened cablelayer with much accomodation amidships and sometimes used for flexible flowline laying.

SP3. TENEO   3051 grt   81.0 x 14.0 x 5.0

E Diesel-electric. Four Normo 6-cylinder oil engines driving four generators connected to 2 electric motors by Bergen Diesel A/S. Machinery aft. 14.5 knots.

CT (2), **BS** (2), **SS** (1), cable machinery in enclosed main cable deck.

1992 - Completed by Hijos de J. Barreras S.A., Vigo for Telecommunicaciones Marinas S.A., Santa Cruz de Tenerife as a cablelayer/repairer and available for use in flexible flowline laying.

SP4. IBERUS   8310 grt   129.22 x 19.23 x 6.3

E Two MaK 6-cylinder oil engines, controllable pitch propeller, forward thruster.

CT (3) with capacity for 6500 km of lightweight fibre optic cable. **SS** (2) portside cablelaying system, starboard side cablelaying and repairing. 25-tonne 'A' frame, plough.

1978 - Completed by Rauma Repola O/Y, Finland as ro-ro *Buraidah*

1979 - Sold to Bore Line O/Y, Helsinki renamed *Bore Sea*

1985 - Sold to Cie de Navigation Transoceanique Suisse S.A., Geneva renamed *Villars*

23.4.1998 - Arrived Vigo for conversion into a cableship for Telecommunicaciones Marinas S.A., Madrid. Renamed *Iberus* on completion during 3.1999.

ST. VINCENT & GRENADINES

SV1. MISS CLEMENTINE 3637 grt   75.0 x 18.3 x 8.2
E Four Caterpillar 8-cylinder oil engines 4080 bhp. Two directional propellers.
1996 - Completed by President Marine Pte Ltd, Singapore as deck cargo pontoon CLB 1.
1998 - Converted into a cablelayer/repairer for Armement Maurel et Prom et Cie, Kingstown, St. Vincent & Grenadines.

SV2. MISS MARIE   3639 grt   75.0 x 18.3 x 8.2
E Diesel-electric. Four Caterpillar 8-cylinder oil engines driving four generators connected to four electric motors. Two forward propellers & two aft.
1998 - Completed in Indonesia for Armement Maurel et Prom et Cie, Kingstown, St. Vincent & Grenadines as a cablelayer/repairer.

SWEDEN

SW1. WARTENA   407 grt   48.75 x 7.75 x 3.15
E 5-cylinder oil engine of 375 bhp. 9.5 knots.
CT (2), 2 cable winches & 2 derricks.
1958 - Completed by Scheeps. Bijlsma & Zonen N.V., Wartena as a motor coaster for J.J. Onnes, Groningen and later converted into a cablelayer for Karlskrona Kommun Stadsbyggnadskontoret, Karlskrona.

SW2. PLEIJEL   1650 grt   71.0 x 13.0 x 3.7
E 10-cylinder Alpha oil engine, 12 knots.
CT (2), **BS** (2)
1972 - Completed by Sonderborg Skibs A/S, Sonderborg as *Ulla Bech* for commercial trading by O.H. Rasmussen, Denmark.
1980 - Sold to Mortensen & Lange, Copenhagen renamed *Kristine Sobye*, 499 grt.
1989 - Sold to Telefinans A/B, Stockholm and converted for cable work renamed *Pleijel*. Used for coastal cables to Gotland and other Baltic islands.

U.S.S.R.

RU1. INGUL 5644 grt   427.9 x 56.6 x 17.1
E Diesel-electric propulsion, twin screw, 14 knots.
CT (3), **BS** (2). 'Klasma' class cablelayer
14.4.1962 - Launched and 12.1962 completed by Wartsila Helsingforsvarvet, Helsinki for cable work connected with domestic telephone network. Type 1 cablelayer. Previously Russia had owned only one small cablelayer in her Navy for harbour defence purposes.

RU2. YANA   5644 grt   427.9 x 52.6 x 17.1
E Diesel-electric propulsion, twin screw, 14 knots.
CT (3), **BS** (2). 'Klasma' class cablelayer
1.11.1962 - Launched and 6.1963 completed by Wartsila Helsingforsvarvet, Helsinki for cable work connected with domestic telephone network. Sister of *Ingul* (Type 1).

RU3. TSNA   6020 grt   427.9 x 52.8 x 17.0
E Diesel-electric propulsion, twin screw, 14 knots.
CT (3), **BS** (2). 'Klasma' class cablelayer
4.4.1968 - Launched and completed 8.1968 by Wartsila A/B, Turku as the first Type 2 cablelayer with different diesels and a larger area of the main deck covered in for cable work, also with a stern gantry.
1997 - Transferred to Ukraine Govt., renamed *Novy Bug*.

RU4. DONETS   6020 grt   427.9 x 52.8 x 17.0
E   Diesel-electric propulsion, twin screw, 14 knots.
CT (3), **BS** (2). 'Klasma' class cablelayer
17.12.1968 - Launched and completed in 7.1969 by Wartsila A/B, Turku as a Type 2 cablelayer, sister of *Tsna*.

RU5. ZEYA   6020 grt   427.9 x 52.8 x 17.0
E Diesel-electric propulsion, twin screw, 14 knots.
CT (3), **BS** (2). 'Klasma' class cablelayer
14.7.1970 - Launched and completed in 11.1970 by Wartsila A/B, Turku as a Type 2 cablelayer, sister of *Tsna*.

RU6. KATUNJ   6020 grt   427.9 x 52.8 x 17.0
E Diesel-electric propulsion, twin screw, 14 knots.
CT (3), **BS** (2). 'Klasma' class cablelayer
20.3.1973 - Launched and completed in 1973 by Wartsila A/B, Turku as a Type 2 cablelayer, sister of *Tsna*. Whilst carrying out a heeling test off the builder's yard on 14.8.1973 she capsized and was refloated two weeks later and reconditioned before delivery.
1995 - Stricken in the Pacific.

RU7. TAVDA   6020 grt   427.9 x 52.8 x 17.0
E Diesel-electric propulsion, twin screw, 14 knots.
CT (3), **BS** (2). 'Klasma' class cablelayer
1977 - Completed by Wartsila A/B, Turku as a Type 2 cablelayer, sister of *Tsna*, but with more prominent gantry aft.

RU8. INGURI   6020 grt   427.9 x 52.8 x 17.0
E Diesel-electric propulsion, twin screw, 14 knots.
CT (3), **BS** (2). 'Klasma' class cablelayer
1978 - Completed by Wartsila A/B, Turku as a Type 2 cablelayer, sister of *Tsna*, but with a more prominent gantry aft. All eight Type 1 and Type 2 cableships are ice-strengthened and carry 1650 n.m. of cable in their tanks.

RU9. EMBA   2050 displacement   249.0 x 41.3 x 9.8

E Diesel-electric with two 8-cylinder Wartsila Vasa oil engines driving two generators connected to electric motors. Two Voith-Schneider propellers can both be inclined to the ship's path to achieve with the bow thruster a much improved turning circle. Crew 40.

1980 - Completed by Wartsila A/B, Helsinki as a Type 1172 cablelayer with capacity for laying 380 tons of cable in shallow waters. Served with Northern Arctic fleet and transferred to Estonia in 1997.

RU10. SETUN   2050 displacement   249.0 x 41.3 x 9.8

E Diesel-electric with two 8-cylinder Wartsila Vasa oil engines driving two generators connected to electric motors. Two Voith-Schneider propellers can both be inclined to the ship's path to achieve with the bow thruster a much improved turning circle. Crew 40.

1981 - Completed by Wartsila A/B, Helsinki as a Type 1172 cablelayer with capacity for laying 380 tons of cable in shallow waters. Serves with Caspian Sea fleet.

RU11. BIRYUSA   2645 grt   282.0 x 41.3 x 9.9

E Diesel-electric with two 8-cylinder Wartsila Vasa oil engines driving two generators connected to electric motors. Two Voith-Schneider propellers can both be inclined to the ship's path to achieve with the bow thruster a much improved turning circle. Crew 40.

7.1986 - Completed by Wartsila A/B, Helsinki as a Type 1172 cablelayer with capacity for laying 380 tons of cable in shallow waters. Serves with Pacific fleet.

RU12. KEM   2645 grt   282.0 x 41.3 x 9.9

E Diesel-electric with two 8-cylinder Wartsila Vasa oil engines driving two generators connected to electric motors. Two Voith-Schneider propellers can both be inclined to the ship's path to achieve with the bow thruster a much improved turning circle. Crew 40.

10.1986 - Completed by Wartsila A/B, Helsinki as a Type 1175 cablelayer with capacity for laying 380 tons of cable in shallow waters. Serves with Pacific fleet.

APPENDIX   CHARTERED CABLESHIPS

NAME	GRT	PERIOD	CHARTERER	EXPEDITIONS
GOLIATH	Tug	1850	Submarine Telegraph Co.	1850 Channel cable
BLAZER	Hulk	1851	Submarine Telegraph Co.	1851 Channel cable
RED ROVER	Tug	1851	Submarine Telegraph Co.	1851 Channel cable
MONARCH	512	1853/70	Electric & Intl. Tel. Co.	1853 Dutch cables
				1854 Firth of Forth
				1854 Firth of Tay
				1855 Irish cables
				1857 Weymouth/Channel
				1862 Dutch cable
BRITANNIA	254	1852	R.S. Newall & Co.	Holyhead/Howth
WILLIAM HUTT	530	1853/54	"	Dover/Ostend
				Portpatrick/Donaghadee
				Portpatrick/Whitehead
PERSIAN	600	1854	Glass,Elliott & Co.	Spezia/Corsica/Sardinia
RESULT	1465	1854	"	Sardinia/Bone
DUTCHMAN	-	1855	"	Sardinia/Bone
AGAMEMNON	Naval	1857/58	"	1857/58 Atlantic cables
NIAGARA	Naval	1857/58	R.S. Newall & Co.	1857/58 Atlantic cables
SARAH BRYANT	-	1857	Glass,Elliott & Co.	Newfoundland/Breton I.
PROPONTIS	-	1857	"	"
WILLING MIND	Tug	1857	R.S. Newall & Co.	Valentia shore end
ELBA	620	1855/59	"	1855 Black Sea
				1856 Mediterranean
				1859 Greek Islands
ARGUS	-	1855	"	1855 Black Sea
BLAZER(2)	Tug	1857	"	Sardinia/Bone
LEIPSIG	-	1857	"	Atlantic cable recovery
INDUSTRY	-	1858	"	Atlantic cable recovery
WILLIAM CORY	1578	1858/61	Glass,Elliott & Co.	1858 Suffolk/Holland
				1858 Cromer/Emden
				1859 Cromer/Germany
				1861 Algiers/Toulon
				1861 Otranto/Corfu
		1866/70	Telcon	1866 Valentia shore end
				1869 French Atlantic
				1870 British-Indian
OMES	-	1859	W.T. Henley	Bass Strait
STELLA	-	1860	"	Cook Strait
BERWICK	537	1859/62	Glass,Elliott & Co.	Denmark/Heligoland
				Folkestone/Boulogne
				Sweden/Gotland
RESOLUTE	204	1859/62	Glass,Elliott & Co.	Whitehaven/Isle of Man
				Jersey/France
				Llandudno/Lynas

NAME	GRT	PERIOD	CHARTERER	EXPEDITIONS
LADY SEALE	264	1859	Glass,Elliott & Co.	Malta/Sicily
BRUNSWICK	1328	1861	"	Toulon/Corsica
RANGOON	1610	1861	"	Mediterranean
MALACCA	1610	1861	"	Mediterranean
HAWTHORNS	752	1862/65	"	Lowestoft/Zandvoort Sicily/Sardinia Sicily/Algeria
IMPERADOR	-	1860	R.S. Newall & Co.	Red Sea
IMPERADIX	-	1860	"	Red Sea
GREAT EASTERN	18914	1864/73	Telcon	Atlantic cables
			French Atlantic Tel. Co.	Atlantic cables
			Telcon	Bombay/Aden/Suez
			Anglo-American Tel. Co.	Atlantic cables
MEDWAY	1823	1866	Telcon	Atlantic cable
ALBANY	-	1866	Telcon	Atlantic cable
WEYMOUTH	-	1866	W.T. Henley	Cook Strait
CHEVY CHASE	810	1867/68	R.S. Newall & Co.	Great Northern cables
ARCHIMEDES	1086	1867/68	"	"
NARVA	872	1867/68	India Rubber,Gutta Percha	Key West/Havana
FUSILIER	323	1869	"	Scilly Isles
SCANDERIA	1983	1868/72	Telcon	1868 Anglo/Med. 1869 French Atlantic 1870 British-Indian 1871 Greek Islands
BELGIAN	2116	1870/72	Telcon	1870 Anglo/Med 1871 China
MINIA	2061	1871/74	Telcon	1871 China 1872 West Indies 1873 Porthcurno/Vigo
CELLA	-	1871	Hooper's Telegraph Works	China/Japan
VANESSA	1182	1872	Telcon	Newfoundland/Breton I.
AMBASSADOR	692	1873/75	Siemens Bros.	Platino/Brazil
GOMOS	-	1873/75	"	Platino/Brazil
MAZEPPA	1164	1872	"	Montevideo/Chuy
WESTMEATH	3342	1887/90	Cie Francaise des Telegraph	Antilles Halifax/Bermuda
RODDAM	2365	1887/89	"	Antilles
RHIWDERIN	1156	1890	Siemens Bros.	Punta Rassa/Key West
ROCKLANDS	-	1891	Cuba Submarine Tel. Co.	Cienfuegos/Batabano
		1895	"	"
URMSTON GRANGE	3446	1896	Siemens Bros.	Guam/Bonin
GRANDHOLM	-	1897	Hooper's Telegraph Works	Manzanillo/Santiago
DIOLIBAH	1717	1900/05	French Govt.	Mediterranean
ATTIKA	1700	1906	Norddeutsche Seekabelwerke	Gallipoli/Imbros Is.

NAME	GRT	PERIOD	CHARTERER	EXPEDITIONS
MERSEY	1211	1915/17	British Government	Harbour defence at
HODDER	1113	1915/17	"	Scapa Flow and other
+ other ships			"	naval anchorages.
POSEIDON	453	1914/18	German Government	Harbour defence at
+ other ships			"	Bremerhaven etc
KANAL II	216	1917	Norddeutsche See.	German waters
CORDOBA	4889	1918	Norddeutsche See.	German waters
ALSTER	393	1918	Norddeutsche See.	German waters
FLINT	4314	1921	Norddeutsche See.	Netherlands East Indies
HOMEDALE	525	1926	Siemens Bros	Anglo-Belgian shore ends
JOLLY DIANA	449	1929	Siemens Bros	Anglo-Belgian shore ends
MERNOO	2417	1937/45	Australian Government	Bass Strait repairs
KABEL	720	1939/40	Gt. Northern Tel. Co.	Danish waters
KARLA	941	1941/47	"	"
BULAN	1048	1940/45	British Government	Harbour defence
+ other ships				at Scapa Flow etc
NORDERAU	1941	1941/45	German Government	Harbour defence
+ other ships				at Bremerhaven etc
HUMMEL	493	1945/64	Norddeutsche See.	German waters
NORDENHAM	1099	1956/63	Norddeutsche See.	German waters
IRMGARD PLEUGER	1834	c1954	Norddeutsche See.	German waters
NEUENFELDE	219	c1955	Norddeutsche See.	German waters
MALIM	394	1947/56	Cable & Wireless Ltd	Singapore
TUNG SONG	549	1947/56	Cable & Wireless Ltd	Singapore
KING FEISAL I	1025	Post WWII	Cable & Wireless Ltd	Persian Gulf
AL HATHERA	299	Post WWII	Cable & Wireless Ltd	Zanzibar
DAVID M	350	1947/49	Siemens Bros.	Solent power cables
PHOTINIA	7661	1964/65 (+ repair in 1977.)	B.I.C.C. "	Power cables across Cook Strait, New Zealand
		1965	"	Trinidad/Tobago
DOMINENCE	424	1981	BICC Supertension Cables (1980) Ltd	Shetland Is.
LUMINENCE	1928	1983	BICC & Balfour, Kilpatrick Ltd	Cook Strait repair, N.Z.
		1985	" "	Surabaya/ Madura(Java)
NASCENCE	1034	1989	Brit. Telecom	Persian Gulf
MILITENCE	1034	1992	BICC	Orkney Is.